CONTENTS

UNIT 1

UNIT 2

UNIT 3

UNIT 4

The Best Bad Thing   State Names

Dear Mr. Henshaw   More State Names

Ben and Me   Even More State Names

A Wave in Her Pocket   States and Neighbors

UNIT 5

UNIT 6

Words with /a/ and /e/

Pretest Directions

Fold the paper in half. Use the blanks to write each word as it is said to you. When you finish the test, unfold the paper and correct any spelling mistakes. Practice those words for the Final Test.

To Parents,

Here are the results of your child's weekly spelling Pretest. You can help your child study for the Final Test by following these simple steps for each word on the word list:

1. Read the word to your child.
2. Have your child write the word, saying each letter as it is written.
3. Say each letter of the word as your child checks the spelling.
4. If a mistake has been made, have your child read each letter of the correctly spelled word aloud, and then repeat steps 1–3.

Children who read and write at home are usually good spellers. Encourage your child to write something every day. In addition, here is a spelling game you can play with your child.

Parent/Child Activity:

Together, think of at least one rhyming word or phrase for as many spelling words as you can. (Helpful hint: Words that rhyme do not necessarily share the same spelling pattern. For example, *banker* rhymes with *anchor*.)

1. _____	1. hammer
2. _____	2. electric
3. _____	3. member
4. _____	4. hatch
5. _____	5. decorate
6. _____	6. chest
7. _____	7. barrel
8. _____	8. else
9. _____	9. catch
10. _____	10. fancy
11. _____	11. handkerchief
12. _____	12. anchor
13. _____	13. canals
14. _____	14. message
15. _____	15. celebrate

Challenge Words

Challenge Words

astonished

bordered

hoisted

treacherous

shoreline

Words with /a/ and /e/

Pattern in a Box
Write the words that have the short vowel sound and spelling pattern shown in the box.

am 1. _____

an 2. _____

3. _____

4. _____

atch 5. _____

6. _____

ec 7. _____

8. _____

em 9. _____

est 10. _____

Fill in the Blanks
Complete each list word by filling in the correct vowel and consonant.

11. _____ _____ se

12. ch _____ _____ t

13. m _____ _____ sage

14. c _____ _____ ebrate

15. b _____ _____ rel

16. d _____ _____ orate

17. can _____ _____ s

18. el _____ _____ tric

19. _____ _____ chor

20. c _____ _____ ch

Scrambled Words
Each item below is a scrambled word from the box. Unscramble each word and write it on the line. Then circle the letter that makes the /a/ or /e/ sound in each word you write.

beds	manners	deck	pass	fence	rest	helpful	sad	latches	when

21. talhc   _____

22. sda   _____

23. kedc   _____

24. ceenf   _____

25. spas   _____

26. nehw   _____

27. desb   _____

28. fulpelh   _____

29. ster   _____

30. snamern   _____

Words with /a/ and /e/

Use the clues and the list words from the box to complete the crossword puzzle.

anchor	decorate
barrel	electric
canals	hammer
catch	member
chest	message

ACROSS

2. waterways

3. large can or drum

5. one who belongs

6. box or trunk

8. holds a ship in place

10. to make more beautiful

DOWN

1. note

4. kind of toy train

7. carpenter's tool

9. to grab or trap

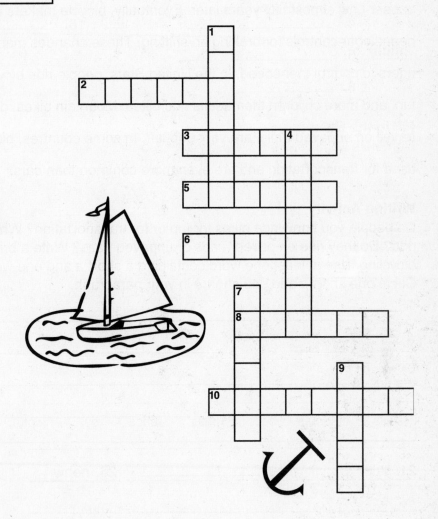

Level 11/Unit 1
Challenge Extension: Have students write entries
for a ship's log, using the Challenge Words.

Words with /a/ and /e/

Proofreading Paragraph

Read the paragraph below. It contains ten spelling errors. Draw a line under each misspelled word and write the correctly spelled word above it.

When the bicycle was inveented, its front wheel was much larger than its rear wheel. The first bicycle with front and rear wheels the same size did not appear until almost fifty years later. Eventually, bicycle makers added heandlebar controls for braking an shifting. These changes made it easier for riders to control ther speed. In the United Stats, people ride bicycles mostly for fun, and more children then adults ride bikes. Mountain bikes, designed for travell on unpaved trails, are vary popular. In some countres, bicycles are widely used for transportation and are even more common than cars.

Writing Activity

Do people you know ride bikes for fun or for transportation? What kind of bikes do they ride? Do they ride on paved roads or unpaved trails? Write a brief paragraph about bicycling. Use at least one word containing a short _a_ and one word containing a short _e_. Circle one short _a_ and one short _e_ in your paragraph.

_____

_____

_____

_____

_____

_____

_____

_____

Macmillan/McGraw-Hill

Words with /a/ and /e/

Complete each spelling word by filling in the missing letters. Then write the complete word on the line.

1. _____ _____ chor

_____

2. b _____ _____ rel

_____

3. can _____ _____ s

_____

4. c _____ _____ ch

_____

5. f _____ _____ cy

_____

6. h _____ _____ _____ er

_____

7. h _____ _____ _____ kerchief

_____

8. ch _____ _____ t

_____

9. h _____ _____ ch

_____

10. d _____ _____ orate

_____

11. c _____ _____ ebrate

_____

12. el _____ _____ tric

_____

13. _____ _____ se

_____

14. m _____ _____ ber

_____

15. m _____ _____ _____ age

_____

ast _____ _____ ished

_____

b _____ _____ dered

_____

h _____ _____ sted

_____

treach _____ _____ ous

_____

sh _____ _____ _____ line

_____

Words with /ô/ and /oi/

Pretest Directions

Fold the paper in half. Use the blanks to write each word as it is said to you. When you finish the test, unfold the paper and correct any spelling mistakes. Practice those words for the Final Test.

1. _____	1. **lawyer** _____
2. _____	2. **hoist** _____
3. _____	3. **employ** _____
4. _____	4. **laundry** _____
5. _____	5. **appoint** _____
6. _____	6. **haul** _____
7. _____	7. **awful** _____
8. _____	8. **poison** _____
9. _____	9. **yawn** _____
10. _____	10. **flaw** _____
11. _____	11. **naughty** _____
12. _____	12. **dawdled** _____
13. _____	13. **crawl** _____
14. _____	14. **oyster** _____
15. _____	15. **foil** _____

Challenge Words

_____

_____

_____

_____

Challenge Words

sliver _____

groping _____

rubies _____

contrary _____

backwoods _____

To Parents,

Here are the results of your child's weekly spelling Pretest. You can help your child study for the Final Test by following these simple steps for each word on the word list:

1. Read the word to your child.
2. Have your child write the word, saying each letter as it is written.
3. Say each letter of the word as your child checks the spelling.
4. If a mistake has been made, have your child read each letter of the correctly spelled word aloud, and then repeat steps 1–3.

Children who read and write at home are usually good spellers. Encourage your child to write something every day. In addition, here is a spelling game you can play with your child.

Parent/Child Activity:
Have your child make up a riddle for each of this week's list words. Then see if you can guess the words from the riddles.

Macmillan/McGraw-Hill

Words with /ô/ and /oi/

What's the Vowel?
Under each word, list the spelling words that contain the same vowel sound.

drawn

1. _____
2. _____
3. _____
4. _____
5. _____
6. _____
7. _____
8. _____
9. _____

coin

10. _____
11. _____
12. _____
13. _____
14. _____
15. _____

Sound It Out
Write the correct spelling of the word that is shown by each phonetic spelling.

1. /hôl/ _____
2. /ə´ point/ _____
3. /oi´ ster/ _____
4. /krôl/ _____

5. /poi´ zən/_____
6. /nô´ tē/ _____
7. /lôn´ drē/_____

Right or Wrong?
Some of the words below are misspelled and some are not. If a word is misspelled, circle it and write it correctly. If a word is correct, write *correct* on the line.

1. hawl _____
2. oyster _____
3. nawghty _____
4. hoist _____
5. poison _____

6. lawyer _____
7. awfull _____
8. foil _____
9. apoint _____
10. crawl _____

Macmillan/McGraw-Hill

Words with /ô/ and /oi/

Read the clues and use the words in the box below to complete the puzzles. Two of the words will be used twice.

appoint	crawl	dawdled	yawn	employ	foil
hoist	laundry	lawyer	naughty	oyster	poison

1. bad
2. move about on all fours
3. aluminum wrap
4. to hire
5. moved slowly

6. dirty clothes
7. harmful substance
8. attorney
9. to lift

10. open mouth when tired
11. to select or assign
12. shelled sea animal

13. to use
14. to carry
15. mollusk

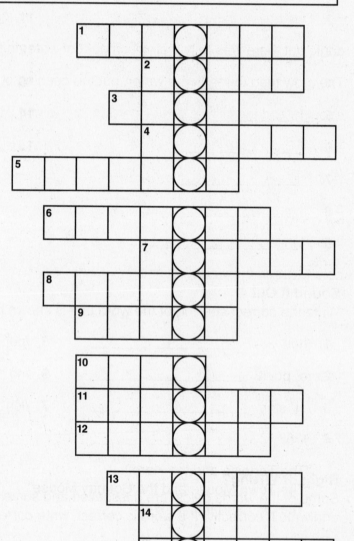

WHAT DID THE GARBAGE COLLECTOR SAY
TO THE THIEF? Write the letters from the circles to find out.

___ ___ ___ ___ ___ ___   ___ ___ ___ ___ ___

___ ___ ___ ___ ___   ___ ___ ___ ___ ___.

Challenge Extension: Have students work in small groups to create a dictionary page with entries for the Challenge Words.

Level 11/Unit 1

16

Words with /ô/ and /oi/

Proofreading Paragraph

Circle each misspelled word in the riddle below. Write the correctly spelled word above the circled error. There are a total of ten misspelled words.

Thirsty Crow

One day, a thristy crow spotted a picher of water and flew down to get a

drink, but there was only a small amount of water in the botom of the pitcher.

The crow tried to reach the water, but the opening of the pitcher wassn't wide

enough, and the crow's beek wasn't long enought. He was just about to give up

on haveing a drink of water when he had an idea. He flew away but then

returned a few minutes latter with something in his mouth, which he threw into

the pitcher. He did this again and again untill, at last, he was able to drink the

water while sitting comefortably on the edge of the pitcher. How was the crow

able to reach the water?

Writing Activity

Some familiar fables are listed below. Write a paragraph, summarizing one of these fables or another one you know. Then look at your paragraph and circle any /ô/ and /oi/ sounds you find.

"The Tortoise and the Hare"
"The Town Mouse and the Country Mouse"
"The Lion and the Mouse"

_____

_____

_____

_____

_____

Words with /ô/ and /oi/

Right or Wrong?

In the list below, some of this week's spelling words are misspelled. If the word is correct, write *C* on the line. If the word is misspelled, circle it and write the correct spelling on the line.

1. dawddled _____
2. foil _____
3. awfull _____
4. hoyst _____
5. crawl _____
6. poison _____
7. yawn _____
8. emploiy _____
9. flaw _____
10. oyster _____

11. lawyer _____
12. appoint _____
13. lawndry _____
14. haul _____
15. naughty _____

   rubies _____

   gropping _____

   contrarry _____

   sliver _____

   backwoods _____

Word Search

There are ten spelling words hidden in each puzzle below. Circle each word that you find. The words may read horizontally, vertically, or backward.

```
J  E  T  T  T  R  M  F  O  M        B  Z  E  U  R  E  V  I  L  S
T  C  K  R  Y  F  Y  C  K  G        N  A  U  G  H  T  Y  O  V  Y
C  R  N  E  F  G  R  O  E  N        H  O  I  S  T  F  P  W  J  M
E  A  F  T  O  L  D  N  R  I        Q  H  C  K  L  U  F  W  A  L
N  W  F  S  I  U  N  T  D  P        I  Q  L  C  K  R  A  A  T  S
O  L  L  Y  L  A  U  R  Q  O        J  T  N  I  O  P  P  A  U  E
S  M  A  O  V  H  A  A  S  R        Y  Y  O  L  P  M  E  B  A  I
I  R  W  X  J  J  L  R  K  G        I  S  D  O  O  W  K  C  A  B
O  V  Y  R  S  L  S  Y  G  V        I  A  M  Y  A  W  N  Z  G  U
P  O  U  D  E  L  D  W  A  D        N  H  L  A  W  Y  E  R  W  R
```

Words with /i/, /ü/, and *gue*

Pretest Directions

Fold the paper in half. Use the blanks to write each word as it is said to you. When you finish the test, unfold the paper and correct any spelling mistakes. Practice those words for the Final Test.

To Parents,

Here are the results of your child's weekly spelling Pretest. You can help your child study for the Final Test by following these simple steps for each word on the word list:

1. Read the word to your child.
2. Have your child write the word, saying each letter as it is written.
3. Say each letter of the word as your child checks the spelling.
4. If a mistake has been made, have your child read each letter of the correctly spelled word aloud, and then repeat steps 1–3.

Children who read and write at home are usually good spellers. Encourage your child to write something every day. In addition, here is a spelling game you can play with your child.

Parent/Child Activity:

Have your child write each spelling word on an index card. Then play a game of "Go Fish." Give each player three cards, and then take turns asking each other for words with certain spelling patterns. For example, you might ask, "Do you have any words with the G-U-E pattern?" The first player to run out of cards is the winner.

1. _____	1. **nickel**
2. _____	2. **ruin**
3. _____	3. **vaguely**
4. _____	4. **driven**
5. _____	5. **bruised**
6. _____	6. **silver**
7. _____	7. **citizen**
8. _____	8. **suitcase**
9. _____	9. **million**
10. _____	10. **mineral**
11. _____	11. **pillow**
12. _____	12. **visible**
13. _____	13. **history**
14. _____	14. **league**
15. _____	15. **cruise**

Challenge Words

_____

_____

_____

Challenge Words

approve

offend

presence

convenience

stern

Words with /i/, /ü/, and *gue*

Fill in the Blanks
Fill in the blanks to complete the list words.

1. _____ i _____ _____ _____ r

6. _____ i _____ _____ ow

2. _____ i _____ _____ ion

7. _____ i _____ i _____ le

3. _____ i _____ _____ _____ al

8. _____ i _____ i _____ _____ n

4. _____ i _____ _____ el

9. d _____ i _____ en

5. _____ i _____ _____ _____ ry

10. _____ _____ gue _____ _____

11. Nine of the words above have something in common. What is it? _____

Pattern Power!
The words below are not on your list, but they share spelling patterns or vowel sounds with list words. Write the spelling pattern in the box. Then write a list word that matches the spelling pattern.

1. tongue [ ] _____

2. wits [ ] _____

3. winner [ ] _____

4. fruit [ ] _____

5. difficult [ ] _____

6. plague [ ] _____

7. trickster [ ] _____

8. juice [ ] _____

9. written [ ] _____

Pick a Pair
In each pair of words below, one word is spelled correctly. Underline the correctly spelled word. Then state whether it has the /i/ sound, the /ü/ sound, or the *gue* pattern.

1. milion   million   _____

2. visable   visible   _____

4. silver   sillver   _____

3. brused   bruised   _____

5. vaguely   vagely   _____

Words with /i/, /ü/, and *gue*

Definitions
Write the list word that matches each definition below.

1. cushion   _____

2. trip   _____

3. rock   _____

4. seen   _____

5. unclearly   _____

6. destroy   _____

7. luggage   _____

8. story of the past   _____

9. coin   _____

10. large number   _____

What Does It Mean?
Write the word in each pair that is related in meaning to the word in dark type.

1. **car**	soap	driven	_____
2. **money**	monkey	nickel	_____
3. **ship**	cruise	shop	_____
4. **hurt**	hurry	bruised	_____
5. **seen**	visible	sea	_____
6. **unclearly**	uncle	vaguely	_____
7. **team**	tea	league	_____
8. **destroy**	ruin	describe	_____
9. **purse**	purple	suitcase	_____
10. **mining**	my	mineral	_____

Level 11/Unit 1
Challenge Extension: Have students group the Challenge Words by the number
of syllables each has, then write the words, dividing them into syllables.

20

Words with /i/, /ü/, and *gue*

Proofreading Paragraph
There are ten spelling errors in the paragraph below. Circle each misspelled word. Then write the correct spelling above it.

Rainy Day Escape

In the furst chapter of C. S. Lewis's "The Lion, the Witch and the Wardrobe," four chuldrun are stuck inside a very unusuall house on a rainy day. With their plans for playing outside ruinned, they decide to make an adventure of exploring the many rooms of the enormous house. One of the children, a girl named Lucy, opens the door to a wardrobe and steps inside. She immediately distcovers that, behind all the hanging clothes, the wardrobe has no back. The next thing she knows, she has entered a misterious forest where snow is falling. This forrest is Lucy's first glimps of the kindgom called Narnia. The other children eventuilly travel to Narnia, too, and C. S. Lewis wrote a total of seven books about their adventures.

Writing Activity
C. S. Lewis believed that everyone has a "secret country." Using at least two of the list words, write a paragraph about an imaginary world of your own.

_____

_____

_____

_____

_____

_____

_____

_____

Words with /i/, /ü/, and *gue*

That's Correct!
In the list below, some of this week's spelling words are misspelled. If the word is correct, write *C* on the line. If the word is misspelled, circle it and write the correct spelling on the line.

1. visible _____
2. citizin _____
3. history _____
4. milion _____
5. minerel _____
6. nickel _____
7. driven _____
8. pillow _____
9. silver _____
10. bruized _____

11. cruse _____
12. ruin _____
13. sutcase _____
14. vagely _____
15. league _____

aprove _____
offend _____
prescense _____
convenience _____
stern _____

Crossword Puzzle
Ten list words are in the crossword puzzle below. Read the clues to fill in the boxes.

DOWN
1. _____ and gold
2. headrest
4. destroy
6. a person who belongs to a country
9. baseball or football _____

ACROSS
3. a _____ dollars
5. overnight bag
7. to insult
8. five cents
10. within view

Words with /j/ Spelled *ge* and *g*

Pretest Directions

Fold the paper in half. Use the blanks to write each word as it is said to you. When you finish the test, unfold the paper and correct any spelling mistakes. Practice those words for the Final Test.

1. _____	1. **margin**
2. _____	2. **region**
3. _____	3. **pageant**
4. _____	4. **average**
5. _____	5. **bandage**
6. _____	6. **barge**
7. _____	7. **fragile**
8. _____	8. **engine**
9. _____	9. **sponge**
10. _____	10. **giraffe**
11. _____	11. **angel**
12. _____	12. **magician**
13. _____	13. **cottage**
14. _____	14. **damage**
15. _____	15. **emergency**

Challenge Words

Challenge Words

_____

destruction

_____

development

_____

flexible

_____

threat

_____

variety

To Parents,

Here are the results of your child's weekly spelling Pretest. You can help your child study for the Final Test by following these simple steps for each word on the word list:

1. Read the word to your child.
2. Have your child write the word saying each letter as it is written.
3. Say each letter of the word as your child checks the spelling.
4. If a mistake has been made, have your child read each letter of the correctly spelled word aloud, and then repeat steps 1–3.

Children who read and write at home are usually good spellers. Encourage your child to write something every day. In addition, here is a spelling game you can play with your child.

Parent Child Activity:
Have your child select ten words from the list. Then ask him or her to see how many other words can be found in each spelling word using only the letters of the word. The letters need to follow the same order.

Macmillan/McGraw-Hill

Words with /j/ Spelled *ge* and *g*

What's That Sound?

Write the nine list words with the *ge* spelling of the /j/ sound. Then think of five words not on the list that contain the same spelling pattern. Circle the *ge* pattern in all the words.

List Words with the *ge* Pattern

1. _____
2. _____
3. _____
4. _____
5. _____
6. _____
7. _____
8. _____
9. _____

Other Words with the *ge* Pattern

10. _____
11. _____
12. _____
13. _____
14. _____

Pattern Power!

Write the six list words with the *g* spelling of the /j/ sound. Then write four words not on the list that contain the same spelling pattern. Circle the *g* pattern in all ten words.

List Words with the *g* Pattern

1. _____
2. _____
3. _____
4. _____
5. _____
6. _____

Other Words with the *g* Pattern

7. _____
8. _____
9. _____
10. _____

Name: _____ Date: _____

Words with /j/ Spelled *ge* and *g*

Write the list word that fits each clue in meaning.

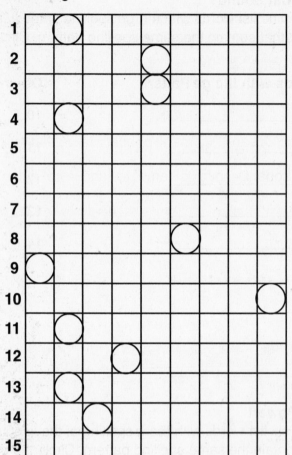

1. wizard
2. tall animal
3. edge of a page
4. territory
5. celebration
6. dish washer
7. _____ food cake
8. breakable
9. makes a car run
10. crisis
11. small house
12. dressing for a wound
13. typical
14. type of boat
15. break

What do you call a child after he or she is four years old? Unscramble the letters in the circles to find out.

A ____ ____ ____ ____ - ____ ____ ____ ____ - ____ ____ ____

Break the Code

Using the code below decode five list words.

1	2	3	4	5	6	7	8	9	10	11	12	13	14	15	16	17	18	19	20	21	22	23	24	25	26
E	Q	W	F	U	B	Y	Z	D	S	A	L	M	O	N	P	H	I	R	T	G	V	X	K	J	C

1. 1-15-21-18-15-1-1-19 _____
2. 18-13-11-21-18-15-1 _____
3. 13-11-21-18-26-18-11-15 _____
4. 19-1-21-18-14-15 _____
5. 9-11-13-11-21-1 _____

Macmillan/McGraw-Hill

Level 11/Unit 1

Challenge Extension: For each Challenge Word, have students write a sentence using the word and a word or phrase that means the opposite.

20

Words with /j/ Spelled *ge* and *g*

Proofreading Paragraph
The paragraph below contains errors in spelling, punctuation, and word usage. Circle each error, and write the correction above the error. There are a total of ten errors.

Hot and Cold Island

Not all islands are tropical. Iceland is a gigentic island in the Arctic regiun of

the atlantic Ocean? Not many people realize that Iceland is actually considered

part of Europe. Despite its name, Iceland is not entirely ice. Although there are

vast glaciers, much of Iceland is made up of tundra, a fragule ecosystem

without much veggetation other then mosses and small shrubs. Like Hawaii,

Iceland has aktive volcanoes and geysers? Many people in Iceland use the

steam and hot water from hot springs—called geothermal energy—to heat their

homes. In 1963, a volcano erupted in the see off the coast of Iceland, and a

new island was born. Iceland, no doubt, could be an interesting place to visit.

Writing Activity
Have you ever visited an island? Using two /j/ words from the group below, write a paragraph about an island, real or imaginary. Subjects you might discuss include what the land looks like, what plants and animals live there, and what kind of weather the island has.

large	change	lounge	emerge	gentle	agency	manage	gem

_____

_____

_____

_____

_____

_____

_____

Words with /j/ Spelled *ge* and *g*

One word in each set is spelled correctly. Write the correctly spelled word on the line.

1. averege averige average avarege _____	**6.** emmergency emergincy emergensy emergency _____	**11.** anjel angle angl angel _____	distruction destruciton destruction destruktion _____
2. bandage bandadge bandige bandege _____	**7.** enjine engine ingene engene _____	**12.** magican magician magacian majician _____	davelopment develpment development developmint _____
3. barg barge bardge barje _____	**8.** fragule fragill fraggile fragile _____	**13.** margine margin marjin margen _____	flexible flexable flexibble flexibel _____
4. cotage cottage cottege cottedge _____	**9.** spunge sponge sponje spunj _____	**14.** pagent padgeant pageant pagint _____	thret tharet thraet threat _____
5. damege dammage damidge damage _____	**10.** girafe girrafe giraffe girraffe _____	**15.** regiun reggion reegion region _____	vareity variaty variety verite _____

Content Words: Countries

Pretest

1. _____   6. _____

2. _____   7. _____

3. _____   8. _____

4. _____   9. _____

5. _____   10. _____

Lost Cities

All of the cities below are capital cities of the places on this word list. Use a map of the world or an atlas to help you complete these pairs.

London, _____   Nairobi, _____

Paris, _____   Tokyo, _____

Lisbon, _____   Madrid, _____

Washington, D.C., _____

Country Hunt

Nine of the words on this list are hidden in this grid. Circle the words as you find them. Then read the remaining letters in order, from left to right, to find the names of the capital city, continent, and chief agricultural product of one of the countries. Which country is it?

```
E  N  G  L  A  N  D  P  E  K
K  I  S  E  N  E  G  A  L  E
J  P  O  R  T  U  G  A  L  N
A  C  H  I  N  A  N  G  A  Y
P  C  O  S  T  A  R  I  C  A
A  F  R  A  N  C  E  S  I  A
N  R  S  P  A  I  N  I  C  E
```

_____

Content Words: Countries

Word List

1. United States
2. Portugal
3. Costa Rica
4. Kenya
5. China
6. England
7. Spain
8. France
9. Japan
10. Senegal

Important Imports

A Mexican piñata is filled with fruit, candy, and gifts, but where does it come from? Mexico, of course. The name of a country is a noun, but it can be turned into an adjective to describe anything from that place. Use your dictionary to find these adjective forms.

a _____ cheese (from France)

some _____ olives (from Spain)

a _____ television (from Japan)

a _____ coffee (in Costa Rica)

an _____ castle (in England)

a _____ sailing ship (from Portugal)

Where Is It?

Two of the countries listed are found on islands and the rest are found on the mainland of continents. Use this chart to sort out which is which.

Islands	Europe	Asia	Africa	North America
_____	_____	_____	_____	_____
_____	_____		_____	Central America
_____				_____

Proofer In Action

Circle the spelling mistakes in these descriptions of flags. Then write each word correctly.

The Chineese flag is red and yellow. _____

The flag of the Untied States is red, white, and blue. _____

The red circle on the Japinese flag represents a rising sun. _____

The flag of Senagal is green and yellow and has red stripes with a green star. _____

Review Words

Pretest

1. _____   6. _____   11. _____

2. _____   7. _____   12. _____

3. _____   8. _____   13. _____

4. _____   9. _____   14. _____

5. _____   10. _____   15. _____

Pattern Power!

These words don't come from the spelling list, but they share some of the same spelling patterns. Say each word aloud. Then find the word or words from the list that share the spelling pattern in dark type. Circle the pattern in each word.

broke _____   _____

mi**st**er _____   _____   _____

ur**ge** _____   _____

element _____

ca**tch** _____

Your Tour Guide

Dictionary guide words help you find your way. Which list word will you find between each pair of guide words?

paddle/paint _____   latter/lavender _____

fragment/fray _____   pork/pose _____

lead/leapt _____   embroidery/emery _____

Word Journal

Which of the words from the list are the hardest for you to spell? Write those words below. What makes these words tricky? Can you think of a rule or a sentence that will help you to remember the pattern? For example, if you forget the e in pageant, remember the phrase "a page at the pageant."

_____

_____

_____

Review Words

Word List

1. hatch
2. region
3. electric
4. hoist
5. Portugal

6. history
7. emergency
8. pageant
9. haul
10. league

11. France
12. bruised
13. celebrate
14. United States
15. laundry

Straighten Up!
Rearrange these letters to form list words.

ogrein _____

lahu _____

chath _____

uaglee _____

thosiry _____

yarduln _____

Tongue Twister
Many words that begin with the same letter or contain similar sounds can be hard to say together. Using some similar-sounding words, compose a tongue twister and write it below.

_____

_____

Proofer in Action
Circle the spelling errors in this scene between June and Lisa. Write the correctly spelled words on the lines.

June: I broosed my leg in France last week. _____

Lisa: Did you see a doctor? _____

June: It was not an emerjency. I had just finished my lawndry, and when I tried to hual it upstairs, I fell. _____

Lisa: I just want to cellebrate that you are okay. _____

June: The bruise was gone before I got back to the Unitid States. _____

Macmillan/McGraw-Hill

Words with *-ture, -sure, -cher*

Pretest Directions

Fold the paper in half. Use the blanks to write each word as it is said to you. When you finish the test, unfold the paper and correct any spelling mistakes. Practice those words for the Final Test.

To Parents,

Here are the results of your child's weekly spelling Pretest. You can help your child study for the Final Test by following these simple steps for each word on the word list:

1. Read the word to your child.
2. Have your child write the word, saying each letter as it is written.
3. Say each letter of the word as your child checks the spelling.
4. If a mistake has been made, have your child read each letter of the correctly spelled word aloud, and then repeat steps 1–3.

Children who read and write at home are usually good spellers. Encourage your child to write something every day. In addition, here is a spelling game you can play with your child.

Parent/Child Activity:
Set a timer for five minutes and see how many words your child can think of that end with /ə/ spelled *-ture* or *-cher*.

1. _____	1. **future**
2. _____	2. **pressure**
3. _____	3. **pitcher**
4. _____	4. **posture**
5. _____	5. **pasture**
6. _____	6. **nature**
7. _____	7. **adventure**
8. _____	8. **bleachers**
9. _____	9. **feature**
10. _____	10. **pictures**
11. _____	11. **mixture**
12. _____	12. **teacher**
13. _____	13. **assure**
14. _____	14. **lecture**
15. _____	15. **capture**

Challenge Words

_____	**dangled**
_____	**deliveries**
_____	**donate**
_____	**publicity**
_____	**organized**

Words with *-ture, -sure, -cher*

Pattern Power!
Write the list words that contain the spelling patterns below.

-cher	*-sure*
1. _____	4. _____
2. _____	5. _____
3. _____	

-ture

1. _____	6. _____
2. _____	7. _____
3. _____	8. _____
4. _____	9. _____
5. _____	10. _____

Sound It Out!

1. /nā´ chər/ _____
2. /pas´ chər/ _____
3. /tē´ chər/ _____
4. /kap´ chər/ _____
5. /fē´ chər/ _____

6. /pik´ chərz/ _____
7. /blē´ chərz/ _____
8. /pres´ shər/ _____
9. /pī´ chər/ _____
10. /mix´ chər/ _____

Fill in the Blanks
Fill in the blanks to form a list word, then rewrite the word on the line.

1. ____ u ____ ____ ____ ____ _____
2. p ____ ____ ____ ____ ____ _____
3. ____ ____ ____ s ____ ____ ____ _____
4. ____ ____ e ____ ____ ____ ____ _____
5. ____ ____ s ____ ____ ____ ____ _____

Macmillan/McGraw-Hill

Words with *-ture, -sure, -cher*

Fill in the Blanks
Write the list word that best completes each sentence.

1. Dancers usually have excellent _____.

2. We sat in the _____ to watch the basketball game.

3. My guitar _____ is a professional musician.

4. The sheep are grazing in the north _____.

5. Spoon the _____ into muffin tins and bake for fifteen minutes.

6. The object of this game is to _____ all of the other players' pieces.

7. Luis took four _____ of the same mountain.

8. This stereo's most useful _____ is its remote control.

9. Jim was the _____ for the first three innings.

10. When Dad stopped for gas, he checked the air _____ in the front tires.

Game, Set, and Match!
Write the list word that fits each clue. Then fill in the boxes below to find the name of a popular sport.

1. combination   ___ ___ ___ ___ ☐ ___ ___ ___ ___

2. upright position ___ ___ ___ ___ ___ ___ ___ ☐

3. past, present, and _____ ___ ___ ___ ___ ___ ___

4. exciting outing ___ ___ ___ ☐ ___ ___ ___

5. take prisoner   ___ ___ ___ ___ ___ ___ ___

6. the world outdoors ☐ ___ ___ ___ ___ ___

7. meadow   ___ ___ ___ ___ ___ ___

8. photographs   ___ ☐ ___ ___ ___ ___ ___

9. speech or talk ___ ___ ___ ___ ___ ___ ___

10. tension or stress ___ ___ ☐ ___ ___ ___ ___

ANSWER: _____

Macmillan/McGraw-Hill

20

Level 11/Unit 2
Challenge Extension: Have students use as many of the Challenge Words as
they can to write a news story about the work of a local volunteer group.

27

Words with *-ture, -sure, -cher*

Proofreading Paragraph

There are ten misspelled words in the paragraph below. Circle each misspelled word.
Then write the correctly spelled word above it.

Rules of the Game

Did you know that baskettball is a relatively new sport? It was invented a hundred

years ago by James Naismith, a teachur in Massachusetts, who wanted his studunts to

have a safe indoor sport to play during the long New England winter. He hoped to capsure

the excitemint of outdoor sports and at the same time make shure that players would not

get hurt. If the inventor of basketball could have visited a gym of the futture, the game we

play today would still look very familiar to him. Although some rules have changed over the

years, one feachure that remains the same is the hite of the basket. Early games used a

peach basket hung so that its rim was ten feet off the flor, and baskets today are still the

same height.

Writing Activity

Write a paragraph about a sport that interests you. It can be an indoor sport or an outdoor
sport, a sport you like to play or one you like to watch. Try to use at least two words that
contain the *-ture* or *-sure* spelling patterns.

_____

_____

_____

_____

10

Words with *-ture, -sure, -cher*

Write or Wrong?
In the list below, some of this week's spelling words are misspelled. If the word is correct, write *C* on the line. If the word is misspelled, circle it and write the correct spelling on the line.

1. leckture _____
2. adventure _____
3. capsure _____
4. feature _____
5. pictcures _____
6. future _____
7. posture _____
8. mixture _____
9. natur _____
10. pasture _____

11. asure _____
12. presure _____
13. bleachers _____
14. pitcher _____
15. teacher _____

danggled _____
deliverys _____
donate _____
publicity _____
orgainized _____

Giddy Up!
Write the list word you would find between each pair of words in a dictionary. The boxed letters answer the riddle.

1. pirate/pizza _____ _____ [ ] _____ _____
2. dolphin/donkey _____ [ ] _____ _____ _____
3. adult/afraid _____ _____ _____ [ ]
4. picnic/pie _____ _____ _____ [ ]
5. feather/fence _____ [ ] _____ _____ _____

WHAT ANIMAL GOES TO BED WITH ITS SHOES ON?

A _____ _____ _____ _____ _____

Words with *-ant* and *-ent*

Pretest Directions

Fold the paper in half. Use the blanks to write each word as it is said to you. When you finish the test, unfold the paper and correct any spelling mistakes. Practice those words for the Final Test.

1. _____	1. servant
2. _____	2. excellent
3. _____	3. patient
4. _____	4. ancient
5. _____	5. current
6. _____	6. content
7. _____	7. constant
8. _____	8. frequent
9. _____	9. pleasant
10. _____	10. instant
11. _____	11. confident
12. _____	12. elegant
13. _____	13. elephant
14. _____	14. president
15. _____	15. different

Challenge Words

_____

_____

_____

_____

_____

Challenge Words

abandoned

erected

heritage

landscape

restore

To Parents,

Here are the results of your child's weekly spelling Pretest. You can help your child study for the Final Test by following these simple steps for each word on the word list:

1. Read the word to your child.
2. Have your child write the word, saying each letter as it is written.
3. Say each letter of the word as your child checks the spelling.
4. If a mistake has been made, have your child read each letter of the correctly spelled word aloud, and then repeat steps 1–3.

Children who read and write at home are usually good spellers. Encourage your child to write something every day. In addition, here is a spelling game you can play with your child.

Parent/Child Activity:
Take turns making up sentences, using one *-ent* spelling word and one *-ant* spelling word in each sentence.

Macmillan/McGraw-Hill

Words with *-ant* and *-ent*

Fill in the Blanks
Fill in the blanks to form list words that follow the spelling pattern shown.

_____ _____ _____ _____ **e n t**

_____ _____ _____ _____ _____ **d e n t**

_____ _____ _____ _____ **e n t**

_____ _____ _____ _____ _____ _____ **e n t**

_____ _____ _____ _____ _____ **a n t**

_____ _____ _____ _____ **a n t**

_____ _____ _____ _____ _____ **a n t**

_____ _____ _____ _____ _____ **a n t**

What's the Noun?
Write a noun based on each adjective below. The first two are done for you.

elegant   elegance

current   currency

1. confident   _____

2. excellent   _____

3. different   _____

4. frequent   _____

5. patient   _____

6. fluent   _____

Write a word that ends in *-ant* or *-ent* based on each of the verbs below. The first five are list words.

1. please _____   **5.** serve _____

2. preside _____   **6.** study _____

3. excel _____   **7.** depend _____

4. confide _____   **8.** assist _____

Words with *-ant* and *-ent*

Replacements

Write the spelling word that can replace the underlined word or words in each sentence below. Some words are used more than once.

1. Jaime was <u>sure</u> he would win the spelling bee. _____

2. Cheri's grandparents live downstairs, so she pays them <u>many regular</u> visits.

   _____

3. My mother asked the store for an <u>immediate</u> delivery.

   _____

4. Marella is the new <u>leader</u> of our ecology club. _____

5. While Mr. Goodwin was in Mexico, he visited <u>very old</u> Aztec ruins.

   _____

6. The librarian is very <u>tolerant</u> when the preschoolers talk during story hour.

   _____

7. Last month's newsletter contained more useful information than the <u>present</u> issue.

   _____

8. On her birthday, my baby sister was <u>happy</u> just playing with the wrapping paper.

   _____

9. Gabriel's two cats look alike, but they have very <u>distinct</u> personalities.

   _____

10. The wedding reception was a very <u>graceful and lavish</u> affair. _____

11. The bridge was out, so we took an <u>alternate</u> route home. _____

12. I am <u>certain</u> I can finish the project before the deadline. _____

13. We spent a very <u>enjoyable</u> morning combing the beach for shells.

    _____

14. Maria's aunt bakes <u>superb</u> apple pie. _____

Challenge Extension: Have students use the Challenge Words to write
a paragraph about some historic site in your state or community.

Level 11/Unit 2

14

Macmillan/McGraw-Hill

Words with *-ant* and *-ent*

Proofreading Paragraph
There are fifteen spelling errors in the paragraph below. Circle each misspelled word.
Write the correctly spelled word above the circled word.

Food for Thought

If you want to work in a restarant, you must have many differant kinds of

skills. Whether the restaurant is casual or elegent, it is very importint to have a

pleasant personality. Remember, you will be in constent contac with many other

people, both in the kitchen and in the dinning room. Also, you must have

excelent math skills to work with money, as well as have the ability to handel

frequant interruptions from custumers. You also must have the ability to be

patiant because problems that are beyond yur control will arise often. Perhaps

most importent of all, you must have a confidant manner.

Writing Activity
Write a paragraph about your favorite holiday meal. Be sure to discuss specific things you
like, such as having guests for dinner, family traditions, the way the dining room is
decorated, or your favorite dessert. Then look at your paragraph and circle any words you
used with the *-ant* and *-ent* spelling patterns.

_____

_____

_____

_____

_____

_____

_____

_____

_____

_____

Words with *-ant* and *-ent*

In the list below, some of this week's spelling words are misspelled. If the word is correct, write *C* on the line. If the word is misspelled, write the correct spelling on the line.

1. president   _____

2. frequint   _____

3. diferent   _____

4. content   _____

5. anceint   _____

6. instant   _____

7. elephant   _____

8. elegent   _____

9. constant   _____

10. pleasent   _____

11. patiant   _____

12. excellent   _____

13. current   _____

14. confident   _____

15. servent   _____

   abandonned   _____

   restore   _____

   landscape   _____

   heritidge   _____

   erected   _____

Words with Double Consonants

Pretest Directions

Fold the paper in half. Use the blanks to write each word as it is said to you. When you finish the test, unfold the paper and correct any spelling mistakes. Practice those words for the Final Test.

To Parents,

Here are the results of your child's weekly spelling Pretest. You can help your child study for the Final Test by following these simple steps for each word on the word list:

1. Read the word to your child.
2. Have your child write the word, saying each letter as it is written.
3. Say each letter of the word as your child checks the spelling.
4. If a mistake has been made, have your child read each letter of the correctly spelled word aloud, and then repeat steps 1–3.

Children who read and write at home are usually good spellers. Encourage your child to write something every day. In addition, here is a spelling game you can play with your child.

Parent/Child Activity:
Take turns acting out the words with your child and guessing what the word is.

1. _____	1. **classroom**
2. _____	2. **wedding**
3. _____	3. **happiness**
4. _____	4. **guess**
5. _____	5. **sudden**
6. _____	6. **stunned**
7. _____	7. **distressed**
8. _____	8. **across**
9. _____	9. **saddle**
10. _____	10. **puzzle**
11. _____	11. **assistant**
12. _____	12. **bass**
13. _____	13. **boss**
14. _____	14. **rattle**
15. _____	15. **tomorrow**

Challenge Words

_____

_____

_____

_____

_____

Challege Words

despair

shriveled

speechless

surveyed

insistent

Macmillan/McGraw-Hill

Name: _____ Date: _____

Double Consonants

Circle the Pattern

Circle the double consonant pattern in each word. Then write the list words that have the same double consonant pattern.

moss

1. _____   waddle   9. _____

2. _____   10. _____

3. _____   11. _____

4. _____   borrow   12. _____

5. _____   grinned   13. _____

6. _____   fizzle   14. _____

7. _____   settle   15. _____

8. _____

It's in the Bag!

Write the list words that fit the spelling patterns. Then unscramble the circled letters to solve the riddle.

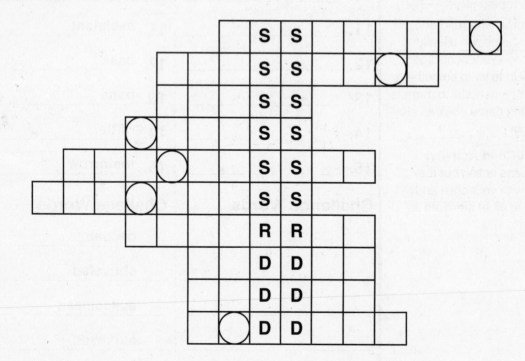

WHAT STARTS WITH A *T*, ENDS WITH A *T*, AND IS FILLED WITH *T*? _____

Double Consonants

Replacements
Write the spelling word that can replace the underlined word or words in each sentence.

1. Marc asked us to <u>estimate</u> how many jellybeans were in the jar. _____

2. Did you hear my sister's bicycle <u>clatter</u> down the sidewalk? _____

3. We were <u>shocked</u> by her rudeness. _____

4. My mother's <u>employer</u> is giving her time off to work at the book fair. _____

5. The water in the stream will rise <u>after today</u>. _____

6. Corrine's duty was to be the teacher's <u>helper</u>. _____

7. Kyle's <u>cheerfulness</u> is contagious. _____

8. James was <u>disturbed</u> by the news of his father's accident. _____

9. She gazed <u>over</u> the lake to the old hotel. _____

10. Allan's decision to quit the team seemed very <u>abrupt</u>. _____

What a Comparison!
Write the spelling word that completes each analogy.

1. _____ is to *school* as *den* is to *home*.

2. *Slow* is to *gradual* as *fast* is to _____.

3. *Seat* is to *bicycle* as _____ is to *horse*.

4. *Robin* is to *bird* as _____ is to *fish*.

5. *Clue* is to *mystery* as *piece* is to _____.

6. *Far* is to *near* as *sadness* is to _____.

7. *Present* is to *future* as *today* is to _____.

8. *Game* is to *child* as _____ is to *baby*.

9. *Graduation* is to *student* as _____ is to *couple*.

10. *Trout* is to *stream* as _____ is to *lake*.

20   Level 11/Unit 2
Challenge Extension: Have students write a
short, scary tale using the Challenge Words.

Double Consonants

Proofreading Paragraph
Correct the fifteen spelling and end punctuation errors in the paragraph below. Circle each misspelled word, and write the correctly spelled word above it. Insert missing end punctuation.

Common Cents

If you are thinking about beginning a new hoby, try collecting pennies. Did

you know that the U.S. Mint does not realy make a coin called a penny The

official name for the coin is *cent*. Many people believe that pennies are made of

coper, but today they are actually made of zinc with only a thin outer layer of

copper Because pennies are so comon, we take them for granted and assume

that they are all alike. If you look carefuly, however, you wil see that every

penny is slightly diferent. In adition to a date, a penny might contain a mint mark

that tels where it was made. Penny collecting is an inexpensive hobby to start

Most large bookstores sel albums for organizing penny colections

Writing Activity
Pretend you have been transported back in time to collect real specimens, not fossils. A tyrannosaur appears! Write a paragraph about what happens next. When you finish writing, look over your paragraph and circle all the double-consonant patterns you find. Then make up a name for the tyrannosaur that has as many double consonants as you can pronounce!

_____

_____

_____

_____

_____

Level 11/Unit 2   15

Macmillan/McGraw-Hill

Double Consonants

One word in each set is spelled correctly. Write the correctly spelled word on the line.

1. stund	6. bosss	11. sutten	despair
stuned	bahs	suden	dispair
stunned	bas	sudden	despare
stunnd	boss	sudenn	dispare

_____ _____ _____ _____

2. distressed	7. classroom	12. saddel	shrivulled
distrest	clasroom	sadle	shriveled
disstressed	klassroom	saddul	shrivuled
distrissed	classrom	saddle	shreveled

_____ _____ _____ _____

3. acrost	8. hapiness	13. puzzul	speechliss
acrass	happiness	puzzel	spechless
across	hapieness	puzzle	speachless
acros	happyness	puzel	speechless

_____ _____ _____ _____

4. asistant	9. geuss	14. raddle	surveyed
assistant	gess	rattle	survayed
assistent	guess	ratle	surveyyed
asistent	gues	rattel	serveyed

_____ _____ _____ _____

5. bas	10. wedding	15. tomorrow	insistant
basss	weding	tommorow	insistent
bass	wehding	tomorow	insisstent
baas	weddeng	tommorrow	inssistent

_____ _____ _____ _____

15 Level 11/Unit 2

More Double Consonants

Pretest Directions

Fold the paper in half. Use the blanks to write each word as it is said to you. When you finish the test, unfold the paper and correct any spelling mistakes. Practice those words for the Final Test.

1. _____	1. balloon
2. _____	2. forgotten
3. _____	3. slippery
4. _____	4. finally
5. _____	5. settlement
6. _____	6. spelling
7. _____	7. allow
8. _____	8. disappear
9. _____	9. bulletin
10. _____	10. umbrella
11. _____	11. rotten
12. _____	12. collision
13. _____	13. billion
14. _____	14. suppose
15. _____	15. lettuce

Challenge Words

Challenge Words	Challenge Words
_____	atmosphere
_____	cycle
_____	data
_____	injured
_____	intense

To Parents,

Here are the results of your child's weekly spelling Pretest. You can help your child study for the Final Test by following these simple steps for each word on the word list:

1. Read the word to your child.
2. Have your child write the word, saying each letter as it is written.
3. Say each letter of the word as your child checks the spelling.
4. If a mistake has been made, have your child read each letter of the correctly spelled word aloud, and then repeat steps 1–3.

Children who read and write at home are usually good spellers. Encourage your child to write something every day. In addition, here is a spelling game you can play with your child.

Parent/Child Activity:

Select a word, then ask your child to select one to make a silly phrase—rotten atmosphere, slippery umbrella. Occasionally challenge your child to spell both words of the silly phrase. Then let your child challenge you.

Macmillan/McGraw-Hill

More Double Consonants

Circle the Pattern
Circle the double-consonant pattern in each word below. Then write the list words that have the same double-consonant pattern.

lollipop 1. _____

2. _____

3. _____

4. _____

5. _____

6. _____

7. _____

8. _____

bitten 9. _____

10. _____

11. _____

12. _____

happy 13. _____

14. _____

15. _____

Fill in the Blanks
Fill in the blanks to complete each spelling word. Then write the word on the line.

1. _____ _____ _____ _____ P P _____ _____ _____   _____

2. _____ _____ T T _____ _____ _____ _____ _____   _____

3. _____ _____ P P _____ _____ _____ _____   _____

4. _____ _____ _____ P P _____ _____ _____   _____

5. _____ _____ L L _____ _____ _____ _____   _____

6. _____ _____ L L _____ _____ _____   _____

7. _____ _____ _____ _____ L L _____   _____

8. _____ _____ L L _____ _____ _____   _____

9. _____ _____ L L _____ _____ _____   _____

10. _____ _____ T T _____ _____ _____   _____

More Double Consonants

What's the Word?
Write the list word that most closely matches each definition.

1. rain protection   _____
2. believe or assume   _____
3. school subject   _____
4. slick   _____
5. agreement   _____
6. decomposed   _____
7. leafy vegetable   _____

8. not remembered   _____
9. at the end   _____
10. vanish   _____
11. crash   _____
12. announcement   _____
13. very large number   _____
14. permit   _____

Finish the Sentence
Write the spelling word that best completes each sentence.

1. The magician seemed to make the rabbit _____.

2. Perry has _____ his grandmother's phone number.

3. The weekly _____ announced the annual chili dinner.

4. She left her _____ in the theater.

5. Shaakir washed the _____ for the salad.

6. We watched the _____ rise high into the clouds.

7. The chemistry lab smelled like

   _____ eggs.

8. Do you _____
   I should wear a jacket?

9. Trying out his new skates, Mickey had a

   _____ with a tree.

10. Ice has made the highway very

    _____.

Challenge Extension: Have students write a short news
or weather report using the Challenge Words.

Level 11/Unit 2

24

More Double Consonants

Proofreading Paragraph
There are ten misspelled words in the paragraph below. Circle each misspelled word.
Then write the correctly spelled word above it.

Keeping Dry

No one knows who invented the umbrella, although umbrellas have been arround for

centuries. There is even an umbrella museum in Italy. Most umbrellas are basicaly the

same except for they're handles. Over the years, people have thought up some prety sily

uses for umbrella handles. Holow handles have held everything from perfume to weapons.

A model stil made today has a pencil compartment in the handle. Superstitions about

umbrellas are comon. Some people believe it is bad luck to open an umbrella indoors. And

opening an umbrella on a suny day is suposed to bring rain.

Writing Activity
Have you ever been caught in a big storm? Does thunder make you nervous? Write a
paragraph about an experience with storms that you have had or someone you know has
had. Use words with double consonants.

_____

_____

_____

_____

_____

_____

_____

_____

More Double Consonants

One word in each pair is spelled correctly and one incorrectly. Draw a line through each incorrectly spelled word. Write each correctly spelled word on the line.

1. collision   colission   _____
2. alow   allow   _____
3. billion   bilion   _____
4. bulletin   bullettin   _____
5. umbrella   umbrela   _____
6. baloon   balloon   _____
7. finaly   finally   _____
8. wrotten   rotten   _____
9. spelling   speling   _____
10. settelment   settlement   _____
11. lettuce   letuce   _____
12. forrgoten   forgotten   _____
13. dissappear   disappear   _____
14. slippery   sliperry   _____
15. suppose   sappose   _____
    atmousphere   atmosphere   _____
    cycle   sycle   _____
    data   datta   _____
    injurred   injured   _____
    intence   intense   _____

Content Words: Body Words

Pretest

1. _____   6. _____

2. _____   7. _____

3. _____   8. _____

4. _____   9. _____

5. _____   10. _____

Body Rhymes

Words that have to do with the body can be interesting. Read the following riddles that describe three of the list words. Using the riddle information will help you unscramble the letters to find out which word fits.

Fun in the sun can lead to one.	**creelfk**	_____
They smell a pear or get some air.	**rtonliss**	_____
It guards the sight and shuts out the light.	**ydeiel**	_____
Where could it be? Just under the knee.	**nhis**	_____
To polish, file, or clip, it's at your fingertip.	**grineiflan**	_____

How Many Syllables?

Do you think that a long word has more syllables than a short word? Usually it does, but not always. To decide how many syllables a word has, count how many separate sounds, are in the word. Read the list aloud. Decide how many syllables each word has. You can use your dictionary to help you.

List words with **one** syllable:

_____   _____   _____

List words with **two** syllables:

_____   _____   _____

_____   _____   _____

List words with **three** syllables:

_____   _____

Content Words: Body Words

Word List

1. fingernail
2. eyelid
3. thigh
4. abdomen

5. knuckle
6. forearm
7. nostrils

8. shin
9. pulse
10. freckle

The Body Shop

Complete the following sentences with a word relating to a body. Choose your answer from the list.

A nurse uses her watch when she checks her patient's _____.

The middle of a human body or the end part of an insect body is called an _____.

Between the ankle and the knee is the _____.

You can find one _____ and more than one _____ on each finger.

Proofer in Action

An exercise instructor has written down some suggestions for a new student. He doesn't realize that he made some spelling mistakes. Can you help? Circle the mistakes. Then write each word correctly.

To warm up, run in place until your puls _____ increases and you feel a

tightening in your upper thy. _____

For a flat tummy, exercise your abomon. _____

Lift dumbbells every day to strengthen your fourarm. _____

Remember to breathe in lots of air through your nostrels while you work out.

_____

Review Words

Pretest

1. _____   9. _____
2. _____   10. _____
3. _____   11. _____
4. _____   12. _____
5. _____   13. _____
6. _____   14. _____
7. _____   15. _____
8. _____

Pattern Power!
Write the list words that contain each of these spelling patterns.

ss		ure

_____   _____

_____   _____

_____

A Lot of Alliteration
Alliteration is the repetition of beginning sounds. You'll see a lot of it in poetry, but many different kinds of writers use it to grab the reader's attention. Look at these sample sentences:

My mother made me mow the lawn.
I bought a big brown bear.

Use list words to write three alliterative sentences.

_____

_____

_____

_____

Review Words

Word List

1. pleasant
2. bulletin
3. suppose
4. frequent
5. knuckle
6. bass
7. pressure
8. forgotten
9. pulse
10. sudden
11. classroom
12. fingernail
13. capture
14. patient
15. bleachers

What's Missing?
Use list words to fill in the blanks.

A _____ noise startled us.

The doctor felt his _____.

I scratched off the tag with my _____.

The special _____ warned that a blizzard was on the way.

We had _____ to hide the presents.

You can't shoot a marble if you can't bend your _____.

The fans filled the _____ to watch the game.

Proofer in Action
This letter of complaint will have a better effect if the spelling is corrected. Can you fix it? Circle the eight incorrectly spelled words and insert the corrections.

Dear Yippee Toys:

As a frecuent buyer of your toys, I suposse I have a right to complain when one is bad. I

expected many plezant hours of play when I bought your Gizzmo Ring. But this toy always

gets stuck on my fingernale or my nukkle. Though I am a very pashent person, I want to

preshure you into writing a buliten warning all kids not to buy this toy.

Yours,

Brad Fox

Macmillan/McGraw-Hill

Compound Words

Pretest Directions

Fold the paper in half. Use the blanks to write each word as it is said to you. When you finish the test, unfold the paper and correct any spelling mistakes. Practice those words for the Final Test.

To Parents,

Here are the results of your child's weekly spelling Pretest. You can help your child study for the Final Test by following these simple steps for each word on the word list:

1. Read the word to your child.
2. Have your child write the word, saying each letter as it is written.
3. Say each letter of the word as your child checks the spelling.
4. If a mistake has been made, have your child read each letter of the correctly spelled word aloud, and then repeat steps 1–3.

Children who read and write at home are usually good spellers. Encourage your child to write something every day. In addition, here is a spelling game you can play with your child.

Parent/Child Activity:

See how many nonsense compounds you and your child can come up with by combining parts of the list words. Then have your child think of definitions for the new compound words. For example, *long detector* could mean *ruler*.

1. _____	1. **tax collector**
2. _____	2. **close-up**
3. _____	3. **long distance**
4. _____	4. **pole-vaulter**
5. _____	5. **tape recorder**
6. _____	6. **movie theater**
7. _____	7. **skydivers**
8. _____	8. **roller skating**
9. _____	9. **thunderhead**
10. _____	10. **lie detector**
11. _____	11. **thirty-third**
12. _____	12. **onlookers**
13. _____	13. **basketball**
14. _____	14. **merry-go-round**
15. _____	15. **sister-in-law**

Challenge Words

_____
_____
_____
_____
_____

Challege Words

accurate

athletic

glory

previous

swollen

Compound Words

Write each list word under the correct heading.

Open Compounds

1. _____

2. _____

3. _____

4. _____

5. _____

6. _____

7. _____

Hyphenated Compounds

8. _____

9. _____

10. _____

11. _____

12. _____

Closed Compounds

13. _____

14. _____

15. _____

Write the list word that follows the pattern of each compound word below.

1. ice skating   _____

2. garbage collector   _____

3. mother-in-law   _____

4. twenty-fifth   _____

5. long-jumper   _____

6. baseball   _____

7. video recorder   _____

8. metal detector   _____

9. puppet theater   _____

10. far-off   _____

Compound Words

Replacements
Write the spelling word that can replace the underlined word or words in each sentence.

1. A crowd of <u>spectators</u> gathered around the juggler. _____

2. We headed home when we saw a <u>storm cloud</u> forming in the western sky. _____

3. Carol is knitting a sweater for her <u>brother's wife</u>. _____

4. The children did not want to stop riding the <u>carousel</u>. _____

5. On the way home, we saw <u>parachutists</u> jumping from a plane. _____

6. My grandfather used to be a <u>government employee</u>. _____

7. The <u>champion</u> easily cleared the ten-foot mark. _____

8. Allyson and Hannah went to the new <u>cinema</u> in the mall. _____

9. Jim brought his <u>stereo</u> to rehearsal. _____

10. Harry S. Truman was the <u>first</u> president of the United States. _____

Cool Puzzler
Use the clues to fill in the puzzle with list words and find the answer to the riddle.

roller   s k a [t] i n g

1. movie   ___ [ ] ___ ___ ___

2. tape   ___ ___ ___ ___ ___ [ ] ___

3. thirty   ___ ___ [ ] ___ ___

4. lie   ___ ___ ___ ___ [ ] ___ ___

5. tax   ___ ___ ___ ___ [ ] ___ ___ ___

WHAT IS THE HARDEST THING ABOUT LEARNING TO ICE SKATE?

___ ___ ___   ___ ___ ___

Macmillan/McGraw-Hill

15 Level 11/Unit 3
Challenge Extension: Have students work in pairs, using the Challenge Words to write an interview with a sports figure.

51

Compound Words

Proofreading Paragraph
There are fifteen errors in the complaint letter below. Circle each mistake, then write the correction above it. Be sure to look carefully at compound words.

Mad About Movies

Mall Magic Movies
123 Hollywood Street
Los Angeles, California 90013

Dear Mall Magic Movies:

My brother and I visited one of your movie-theaters yesterday. It was the twentyfirst time wed seen the film, "The Pole-Vaulter Goes Iceskating." Right away, we notissed that something was wrong with the projector (or the person running it). I can't beleive that he or she din't realize that the movie was upsidedown. The track meat scenes were a dead give away. Allso. the sound was backward or something. We couldn't understand a single word. I hapened to have a taperecorder in my purse, so I made this tape for you. Please listen to it. I think you should honor you're moneyback guarantee.

Your loyal customer,

Mary Merry

Writing Activity
Write a short complaint letter about a product or service. Check your use of any compound words.

_____
_____
_____
_____
_____

Macmillan/McGraw-Hill

Compound Words

Cross It Out

One spelling word in each pair is spelled correctly and one is not. Draw a line through each incorrectly spelled word, and write each correctly spelled word on the line.

1. on-lookers   onlookers   _____

2. skydivers   sky divers   _____

3. baskettball   basketball   _____

4. thunder-head   thunderhead   _____

5. lie detector   lie detecter   _____

6. tax collecter   tax collector   _____

7. pole-vaulter   poll-vaulter   _____

8. thirty-third   thirty third   _____

9. movie theater   movie-theater   _____

10. taperecorder   tape recorder   _____

11. sister-in-law   sister in law   _____

12. close-up   closeup   _____

13. roller skating   roller skatting   _____

14. longdistance   long distance   _____

15. merry-go-round   marry-go-round   _____

    accurate   acurate   _____

    atheletic   athletic   _____

    glorry   glory   _____

    previous   prevous   _____

    swolen   swollen   _____

Past Tenses

Pretest Directions

Fold the paper in half. Use the blanks to write each word as it is said to you. When you finish the test, unfold the paper and correct any spelling mistakes. Practice those words for the Final Test.

1. _____	1. **regretted**
2. _____	2. **slid**
3. _____	3. **ashamed**
4. _____	4. **drove**
5. _____	5. **built**
6. _____	6. **meant**
7. _____	7. **stole**
8. _____	8. **ripped**
9. _____	9. **slept**
10. _____	10. **braced**
11. _____	11. **dreamed**
12. _____	12. **crept**
13. _____	13. **forced**
14. _____	14. **wound**
15. _____	15. **climbed**

Challenge Words

_____	**district**
_____	**emerged**
_____	**monstrous**
_____	**piers**
_____	**scheme**

To Parents,

Here are the results of your child's weekly spelling Pretest. You can help your child study for the Final Test by following these simple steps for each word on the word list:

1. Read the word to your child.
2. Have your child write the word, saying each letter as it is written.
3. Say each letter of the word as your child checks the spelling.
4. If a mistake has been made, have your child read each letter of the correctly spelled word aloud, and then repeat steps 1–3.

Children who read and write at home are usually good spellers. Encourage your child to write something every day. In addition, here is a spelling game you can play with your child.

Parent/Child Activity:
With your child, see how many words can be found using the letters in each list word. For example, *ripped* contains *pie* and *dip,* among others.

Macmillan/McGraw-Hill

Past Tenses

In the Past
Write the list word that forms the past tense of each of the words below.

1. slide _____
2. climb _____
3. force _____
4. brace _____
5. steal _____

6. creep _____
7. sleep _____
8. dream _____
9. regret _____
10. drive _____

Change each sentence to the past tense by writing a list word to replace each underlined word.

1. The dog <u>steals</u> the cat's food. _____

2. Cary <u>dreams</u> about hang gliding. _____

3. My father <u>winds</u> the cable onto a reel. _____

4. Our class <u>builds</u> all the stage sets for school plays. _____

5. Maria <u>rips</u> open the mail right away. _____

6. Julius <u>means</u> to be fair when choosing team members. _____

7. On vacation, my mother <u>drives</u> more than my father. _____

8. Tony <u>regrets</u> missing the computer club meeting. _____

9. During meetings, I <u>slide</u> notes under the office door. _____

10. My little brother <u>sleeps</u> in the back seat on the way home. _____

Write the list word that shares a spelling pattern with each past tense word below. The first one is done for you.

    hid   <u>slid</u>

1. found _____
2. tapped _____
3. dove _____
4. laced _____
5. combed _____

Past Tenses

Write a spelling word to complete each sentence.

1. The cat _____ across the room.

2. Mikail _____ right through the sirens.

3. My grandmother has always _____ not learning how to play an instrument.

4. Tammy _____ a spice rack in her woodworking class.

5. I _____ to tell you that your meeting was canceled.

6. Sara's cat _____ across the living room rug.

7. The class _____ all the way to the top of the monument.

8. Karl _____ across the ice.

9. We _____ nearly seven hundred miles in one day.

10. The stray dog had an open _____ on its leg.

Complete the puzzle with list words by using the clues below.

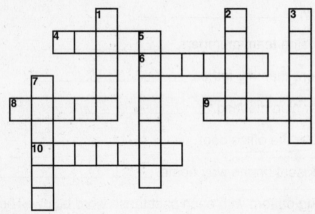

Across

4. coiled or twisted

6. shredded or torn

8. tiptoed

9. robbed

10. rose or went up

Down

1. constructed

2. rested

3. demanded or ordered

5. hoped or imagined

7. strengthened or supported

Level 11/Unit 3

Challenge Extension: Have students work with a partner to create a dictionary page with entries for the Challenge Words.

20

Past Tenses

Proofreading Paragraph
Correct the ten errors in verb tense in the postcard below. Circle each incorrect word and write the correct word above it.

Camping Disaster!

Dear Sam,

So far, our camping trip has been a disaster! First we drove an hour to the

campground only to discovered that we had forgetted our sleeping bags. Mom decides to

go back home and get them while Dad and I setted up the tent. Putting the poles together,

Dad riped a big hole in our tent's screen. While I was looking for the sewing kit I meaned to

pack, a raccoon creeped over and stealed our bag of cookies from the picnic table. Now

we are waiting for Mom to get back and trying to decided whether to go straight back

home.

Your friend,
Jacin

Writing Activity
Write a paragraph about a vacation or trip you have taken or would like to take. Try to use at least five past-tense verbs.

_____

_____

_____

_____

_____

_____

_____

_____

Past Tenses

In the list below, some of this week's spelling words are misspelled. If the word is correct, write *C* on the line. If the word is misspelled, circle it and write the correct spelling on the line.

1. regretted _____

2. slided _____

3. ashamed _____

4. drived _____

5. builded _____

6. meant _____

7. stealed _____

8. ripped _____

9. sleeped _____

10. creeped _____

11. braced _____

12. dreamed _____

13. fourced _____

14. winded _____

15. climbed _____

districk _____

emerged _____

monstrus _____

piers _____

scheme _____

Words Ending in *y*

Pretest Directions

Fold the paper in half. Use the blanks to write each word as it is said to you. When you finish the test, unfold the paper and correct any spelling mistakes. Practice those words for the Final Test.

To Parents,

Here are the results of your child's weekly spelling Pretest. You can help your child study for the Final Test by following these simple steps for each word on the word list:

1. Read the word to your child.
2. Have your child write the word, saying each letter as it is written.
3. Say each letter of the word as your child checks the spelling.
4. If a mistake has been made, have your child read each letter of the correctly spelled word aloud, and then repeat steps 1–3.

Children who read and write at home are usually good spellers. Encourage your child to write something every day. In addition, here is a spelling game you can play with your child.

Parent/Child Activity:

Ask your child to use each adjective on the list to modify a noun of your child's choosing. For example, *furry* might modify *creature*. Review the spelling of each list word used.

1. _____	1. **shaky** _____
2. _____	2. **stingy** _____
3. _____	3. **weekly** _____
4. _____	4. **dizzy** _____
5. _____	5. **drowsy** _____
6. _____	6. **empty** _____
7. _____	7. **energy** _____
8. _____	8. **furry** _____
9. _____	9. **husky** _____
10. _____	10. **lonely** _____
11. _____	11. **worthy** _____
12. _____	12. **windy** _____
13. _____	13. **weary** _____
14. _____	14. **steady** _____
15. _____	15. **sorry** _____

Challenge Words

_____

_____

_____

_____

Challenge Words

basis _____

distinguish _____

reaction _____

technique _____

treatment _____

Words Ending in *y*

Follow the Pattern
Write the list words that contain the following spelling patterns.

-gy   1. _____

2. _____

-dy   3. _____

4. _____

-ky   5. _____

6. _____

-ly   7. _____

8. _____

-ry   9. _____

10. _____

11. _____

-sy   12. _____

-ty   13. _____

-thy 14. _____

-zy   15. _____

Respellings
Write the correct word for each phonetic spelling.

1. /diz´ ē/ _____

2. /wir´ ē/ _____

3. /fer´ ē/ _____

4. /wē´ klē/ _____

5. /win´ dē/ _____

6. /shā´ kē/ _____

7. /həs´ kē/ _____

8. /drou´ zē/ _____

9. /ste´ dē/ _____

10. /stin´ jē/ _____

What's in the Box?
Complete the list words. Then read down the boxed letters to answer the riddle.

1. _____ [____] _____ _____ G Y

2. [____] _____ S K Y

3. [____] _____ _____ T Y

4. S [____] _____ R Y

5. F [____] _____ R Y

6. _____ [____] _____ _____ _____ D Y

7. [____] H _____ K Y

8. _____ [____] _____ Z Y

9. _____ [____] _____ _____ _____ S Y

10. L _____ _____ [____] L Y

Which side of a chicken has the most feathers?

_____ _____ _____ _____   _____ _____ _____ _____ _____ _____ _____ _____

Words Ending in *y*

Word Match

Write the list word that most closely matches the meaning of each word or phrase below.

1. light-headed _____
2. every seven days _____
3. selfish _____
4. solitary _____
5. breezy _____

6. fuzzy _____
7. apologetic _____
8. deserving _____
9. wobbly _____
10. blank _____

Finish the Sentence

Write the list word that best completes each sentence.

1. Julia was _____ she had to miss the field trip to the art museum.

2. Amusement park rides always make Marissa feel _____.

3. My grandmother is bursting with _____ after her nap.

4. When Ben opened the paint can, he discovered that it was _____.

5. Do you believe this project is _____ of first prize?

6. My brother is very _____ with his money.

7. The dance band played music with a _____ beat.

8. Don't forget to study for your _____ spelling test.

9. What are those _____ little animals called?

10. After a week on the island, Steven started to feel _____.

11. It was too _____ yesterday to go sailing.

12. The old wooden ladder seemed a bit _____.

13. The quiet music and the warmth from the fireplace made Kent feel _____.

14. We were all _____ after the long bus ride.

15. Peter had a cold, so his voice was very _____.

25

Level 11/Unit 3
Challenge Extension: Ask students to imagine they are famous scientists
and to use the Challenge Words to write a journal entry about their work.

61

Words Ending in *y*

Proofreading Paragraph
Correct the fifteen errors in the paragraph below. Circle each error and write a correction above it.

On Top of Old Smoky

If heights make you dizy, you probally shouldn't became a fire lookout ranger. These

rangers live for months in mountaintop towers, keeping watch over thousands of acres.

The top of a mountain Can get very windy, so a tower probly feels a little shakey in a

storm. Also. there is nothing fancey about the interior of a lookout tower, It's similar to

camping out for months on end. People always ask rangers if

they get loneley up there for so long, but rangers

claim they are not realy alone. There is usually a

steddy stream of fury visitors to observe—bears,

coyotes, cougars, and moose—as well as an

occasional hikker or backpackers to talk to.

Writing Activity
Would you like a job where you spent most of your time alone? Or would you rather work with people? Write a paragraph using at least three words that end in -*y*.

_____

_____

_____

_____

_____

Macmillan/McGraw-Hill

Words Ending in *y*

Cross It Out

Some of the words below are misspelled. If a word is correct, write *C* on the line. If a word is misspelled, draw a line through it and write the correct spelling on the line.

1. shakey _____
2. stingey _____
3. weekly _____
4. dizzy _____
5. drowsy _____
6. empty _____
7. energy _____
8. furrey _____
9. husky _____
10. loneley _____

11. wurthy _____
12. windy _____
13. wearry _____
14. steddy _____
15. sory _____

basis _____
distingwish _____
reaction _____
technicue _____
treatment _____

Crossword

Use the clues below to complete the crossword puzzle with words from this week's list.

Across

4. worn out
5. power
6. regretful

Down

1. soft and fuzzy
2. sleepy
3. breezy
4. deserving

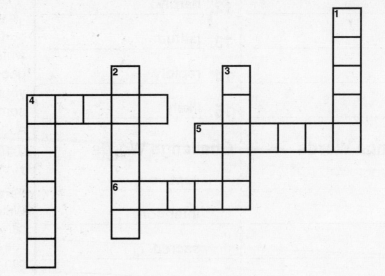

Words Ending in *ly* and *tude*

Pretest Directions

Fold the paper in half. Use the blanks to write each word as it is said to you. When you finish the test, unfold the paper and correct any spelling mistakes. Practice those words for the Final Test.

1. _____	1. **shortly**
2. _____	2. **barely**
3. _____	3. **gratitude**
4. _____	4. **busily**
5. _____	5. **carefully**
6. _____	6. **attitude**
7. _____	7. **daily**
8. _____	8. **easily**
9. _____	9. **longitude**
10. _____	10. **individually**
11. _____	11. **happily**
12. _____	12. **hardly**
13. _____	13. **latitude**
14. _____	14. **rapidly**
15. _____	15. **likely**

Challenge Words	**Challenge Words**
_____	**captive**
_____	**intention**
_____	**sacred**
_____	**starvation**
_____	**critically**

To Parents,

Here are the results of your child's weekly spelling Pretest. You can help your child study for the Final Test by following these simple steps for each word on the word list:

1. Read the word to your child.
2. Have your child write the word, saying each letter as it is written.
3. Say each letter of the word as your child checks the spelling.
4. If a mistake has been made, have your child read each letter of the correctly spelled word aloud, and then repeat steps 1–3.

Children who read and write at home are usually good spellers. Encourage your child to write something every day. In addition, here is a spelling game you can play with your child.

Parent/Child Activity:
Write each spelling word on a card. Then set a timer and see how quickly your child can alphabetize the cards.

Macmillan/McGraw-Hill

Words Ending in *ly* and *tude*

What's the Pattern?
Write the spelling words that contain the *-ly* spelling pattern. Then underline the *-ly* pattern in the words.

1. _____   7. _____

2. _____   8. _____

3. _____   9. _____

4. _____   10. _____

5. _____   11. _____

6. _____

Write the spelling words that contain the *-tude* spelling pattern. Underline the *-tude* pattern in the words.

1. _____

2. _____

3. _____

4. _____

Fill in the Blanks
Fill in the blanks to complete the list words. Then unscramble the boxed letters to find the name of a popular board game.

1. _____ A [_____] I L Y

2. _____ U [_____] I L Y

3. [_____] _____ _____ _____ I L Y

4. [_____] _____ R E _____ _____ L L Y

5. B _____ _____ [_____] L Y

_____ _____ _____ _____ _____ _____

Words Ending in *ly* and *tude*

Adverbs
Write the adverb that is formed when *-ly* is added to the adjective given below. Remember to change *y* at the end of an adjective to *i*.

1. short _____

2. happy _____

3. hard _____

4. careful _____

5. busy _____

Definitions
Write the list word that matches each definition below.

1. one by one _____

2. cheerfully _____

3. effortlessly _____

4. probable _____

5. frame of mind _____

Finish the Sentence
Write the list word that best completes each sentence.

1. My sister Colleen was _____ four years old when we took the training wheels off her bike.

2. The third graders are learning about latitude and _____.

3. Summer vacation is fun, but it always goes by too_____.

4. We spent the day _____ preparing for the party.

5. Denise's friends visited her _____ while she was in the hospital.

6. Drive _____!

7. Jim's lost library card is not _____ to be found.

8. My mother can _____ juggle four beanbags at once.

9. With a positive _____, you are more likely to succeed.

10. Donovan sent a note expressing his _____ for the gift.

Level 11/Unit 3
Challenge Extension: Have students create a crossword puzzle using the Challenge Words.

20

Words Ending in *ly* and *tude*

Proofreading Paragraph
Correct the ten spelling errors in the letter below. Circle each incorrectly spelled word and write the correctly spelled word above it.

A Big Difference

Dear Uncle Ed,

My school ecology club is studying the effects of people's dailly

routines on the environment. We believe that changing people's

attittudes is one important thing we can do to save the earth. We

have developed a survey that can easilly be filled out in five or ten

minutes. Please read all of the questions carefuly. Then examine

your habits criticaly. We are especialy interested in how much

energy and water people use. If you fill out a survey, we will show

our graditude by sharing some of our ideas for adding

environmentaly frendly habits to your everyday life. Most people

are surprised at how much difference they can make with hartly

any effort at all.

Thank you for your help.

Your nephew,

Jamie

Words Ending in *ly* and *tude*

A. One word in each set is spelled correctly. Circle the correctly spelled word.

1. shortlly	**6.** easely	**11.** likly	capteve
schortly	eazily	lickly	captive
shortly	easally	likeley	capetive
shorttly	easily	likly	capptive
2. barly	**7.** individualy	**12.** graditude	intention
barely	endividually	grattitude	intension
bareley	individually	gratitude	intentoin
bairly	endividualy	gratittude	intenton
3. bussily	**8.** hapily	**13.** atitude	sakred
buzily	happily	attittude	sackred
busilly	happaly	attitude	sacred
busily	happilly	additude	sacrid
4. carefully	**9.** hartly	**14.** latitude	starvasion
carfully	hardly	laditude	starrvation
carefuly	hardely	lattitude	stairvation
cairfully	hardley	latittude	starvation
5. daley	**10.** rapidly	**15.** lonjitude	criticaly
dialy	rapedly	longittude	crittically
daily	rappidly	longitude	critically
dailly	rappedly	longetude	criticly

Macmillan/McGraw-Hill

Content Words: Food Names

Pretest

1. _____   6. _____

2. _____   7. _____

3. _____   8. _____

4. _____   9. _____

5. _____   10. _____

Pattern Power

Which food words on the word list have double letters?

_____   _____

What letters are doubled in these words? Write them in these boxes:

☐ ☐

Can you think of other words in which these letters are doubled?

_____

In Case of Emergency

If you forgot how to spell a word, don't panic. Look it up in your dictionary. Which list word would you find between each pair of guide words?

chunk/circus   _____   peace/peck   _____

target/task   _____   pressure/price _____

banquet/bargain   _____   satisfy/servant _____

Word Journal

Which food on the list do you find most interesting? Write that name below. Then brainstorm a list of foods. You can refer to your encyclopedia or other resource materials to find out interesting facts. You might want to know: How did the food get its name? Where does it come from, and where is it grown? How can it be used to make other kinds of foods?

_____

_____

_____

_____

Content Words: Food Names

Word List

1. pretzel
2. pizza
3. pear
4. tart

5. celery
6. cider
7. barbecue
8. cranberry

9. sausage
10. gingerbread

A Delicious Puzzle

All of the words on this list are hidden in these letters. Circle the words as you find them.

```
C  B  R  E  L  D  C  E  P  Q  H  S  E  O
R  R  V  G  I  N  G  E  R  B  R  E  A  D
A  L  A  N  O  Y  M  S  E  A  F  Y  W  E
N  Z  M  N  R  A  B  R  T  R  S  A  M  S
B  T  O  T  B  J  A  C  Z  B  O  R  J  A
C  Z  W  I  A  E  U  C  E  B  R  A  B  U
D  Y  R  Z  P  X  R  G  L  Q  E  T  G  S
V  B  Z  C  E  L  E  R  Y  U  D  A  E  A
C  I  D  E  R  N  O  C  Y  E  I  R  D  G
P  C  H  T  W  I  T  S  Z  N  C  T  V  E
```

Proofer in Action

This menu shows the prices of foods at Snack Hut. But the customers are confused about the food. They're also hungry! If you fix the spellings, you can help them understand the menu. Circle the misspelled words and write the correct spelling on the line below.

Snack Hut

Pizzza - $1.00 a slice

Hot pretsels - .85 cents each

Celerie Sticks - .90 cents

Ginjerbread cookies - .35 cents each

Cranbery juice - .45 cents a cup

Review Words

Pretest

1. _____
2. _____
3. _____
4. _____
5. _____

6. _____
7. _____
8. _____
9. _____
10. _____

11. _____
12. _____
13. _____
14. _____
15. _____

Pattern Power!

Double letters show up in a lot of words. Can you find the list words that match these double letter spelling patterns?

_____ _____ z   z _____

_____ _____ _____ _____ _____ _____ t   t _____ _____

_____ _____ r   r _____

_____ _____ p   p _____ _____

_____ _____ _____ _____ _____ _____ l   l _____ _____

_____ _____ r   r _____ _ _____ _ _____ _____ _____ _____ _____

Double letters rarely come at the beginning of words. Can you think of any words that start with double letters? (Hint: One is right near the beginning of your dictionary!)

_____

One of the Above

Some tests ask you to find words that have similar meanings, called **synonyms**. Shade the circle next to the word that has a similar meaning to the word above it.

stingy
(a) ungenerous
(b) plentiful
(c) share

easily
(a) doubtful
(b) certainly
(c) difficulty

lonely
(a) solitary
(b) unhappy
(c) friendly

carefully
(a) quickly
(b) recklessly
(c) cautiously

Review Words

Word List

1. cranberry	5. lonely	9. easily	13. merry-go-round
2. carefully	6. pizza	10. slid	14. stingy
3. thunderhead	7. furry	11. regretted	15. basketball
4. braced	8. happily	12. barbecue	

Straighten Up!
Rearrange these letters to form list words.

abksebtlal   _____   grertedet   _____

arubeceb   _____   urfry   _____

refulcaly   _____   rycrnbera   _____

You can often find words inside other words. Can you see the word *men* in *document*? Hunt down these hidden words in your list. Which list word contains a word for what goes on top of a peanut butter jar?

list word   _____   hidden word   _____

Which list word contains a word for a running contest?

list word   _____   hidden word   _____

Which list word contains a word that describes being beneath something?

list word   _____   hidden word   _____

Which list word contains a word for a hurt that comes from a bee?

list word   _____   hidden word   _____

Proofer in Action
This script might be used for a radio play. Can you fix the spelling errors? Circle the six misspelled words and write the correct spelling above the word.

Edward: When you slidd into second, I thought you would make it ezily.

Rosa: Yeah, me too, but then when the umpire called "OUT!" I regratted trying to steal the

base. I like baskettball better anyway.

Edward: Me, too. Hey, I'm starving. Do you want to eat lunch?

Rosa: I could easilly eat a whole piza.

State Names

Pretest Directions

Fold the paper in half. Use the blanks to write each word as it is said to you. When you finish the test, unfold the paper and correct any spelling mistakes. Practice those words for the Final Test.

To Parents,

Here are the results of your child's weekly spelling Pretest. You can help your child study for the Final Test by following these simple steps for each word on the word list:

1. Read the word to your child.
2. Have your child write the word, saying each letter as it is written.
3. Say each letter of the word as your child checks the spelling.
4. If a mistake has been made, have your child read each letter of the correctly spelled word aloud, and then repeat steps 1–3.

Children who read and write at home are usually good spellers. Encourage your child to write something every day. In addition, here is a spelling game you can play with your child.

Parent/Child Activity:

Help your child learn the state abbreviations. Call out a two-letter state abbreviation, and have your child say the state name and then write it down. Do this for each state name on this week's list. If you have a map of the United States available, help your child locate each state on the map.

1. _____	1. **Georgia**
2. _____	2. **Alabama**
3. _____	3. **Mississippi**
4. _____	4. **Louisiana**
5. _____	5. **Arkansas**
6. _____	6. **Florida**
7. _____	7. **Indiana**
8. _____	8. **Kentucky**
9. _____	9. **Tennessee**
10. _____	10. **Ohio**
11. _____	11. **Illinois**
12. _____	12. **Michigan**
13. _____	13. **Iowa**
14. _____	14. **Nebraska**
15. _____	15. **Kansas**

Challenge Words

_____

_____

_____

_____

Challenge Words

bachelor

blurted

canvas

mustache

peddler

State Names

Create a State
Choose from the syllables in the box to write ten state names on the lines. Cross out each syllable as you use it.

Al	a	Flor	O	a	i	bras	bam	a	di	da	an	hi
gan	Kan	i	Ken	ka	Ar	o	Lou	l	sas	tuck	kan	si
Ne	sas	In	a	Mich	an	y						

1. _____   6. _____

2. _____   7. _____

3. _____   8. _____

4. _____   9. _____

5. _____   10. _____

Ends in *A*
Write the state names from the list that end with the letter *a*.

1. _____

2. _____

3. _____

4. _____

5. _____

6. _____

7. _____

Ends in *S*
Write three state names from the list that end with the letter *s*.

1. _____

2. _____

3. _____

Macmillan/McGraw-Hill

State Names

On the Map
Write the correct state name for each numbered state on the map.

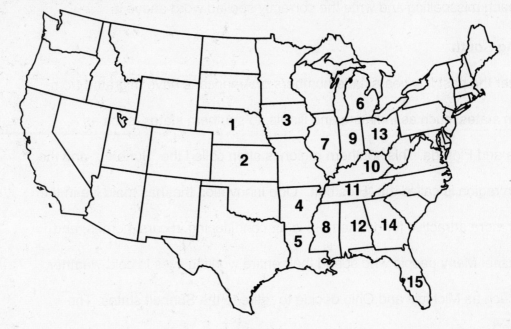

1. _____   9. _____

2. _____   10. _____

3. _____   11. _____

4. _____   12. _____

5. _____   13. _____

6. _____   14. _____

7. _____   15. _____

8. _____

For Short
Write the name of the state for each abbreviation.

1. AL _____   6. IL _____

2. AR _____   7. IA _____

3. KS _____   8. MS _____

4. KY _____   9. OH _____

5. MI _____   10. TN _____

Macmillan/McGraw-Hill

Level 11/Unit 4
Challenge Extension: Have students write and
illustrate a sentence for each Challenge Word.

25

State Names

Proofreading Paragraph

There are ten misspelled words (including some state names) in the paragraph below.
Circle each misspelling and write the correctly spelled word above it.

Flocking South

Over the past fifty years, larje numbers of Americans have migrated from

northern states, such as Indianna and Ilinois, to southern states, such as

Georgia and Florada. This southern region is often called the "Sunbelt," and the

northern region is called the "Frostbelt." One innovation that has maid life in the

Sunbelt more attractive for northerners is air conditioning in cars, homes, and

workplases. Many people who spend their entire working lives in cold-weather

states such as Michigin and Ohio decide to retire to the Sunbelt states. The

warm southern climit alows people to spend more leizure time outdoors.

Writing Activity

Write a paragraph about the weather in your region of the country. Tell what you like and
dislike about it.

_____

_____

_____

_____

_____

_____

_____

_____

_____

State Names

Cross It Out

One word in each pair is spelled correctly, and one is spelled incorrectly. Draw a line through each incorrectly spelled word.

1. Georgia   Goergia
2. Allabama   Alabama
3. Mississippi   Missisippi
4. Louisiana   Lousiana
5. Arkansas   Arkansaw
6. Florrida   Florida
7. Indianna   Indiana
8. Kentucky   Kentuky
9. Tenessee   Tennessee
10. Ohioh   Ohio

11. Ilinois   Illinois
12. Michigan   Michagan
13. Iohwa   Iowa
14. Nebraska   Nebrasska
15. Kansas   Kansass

bachelor   batchelor
blurded   blurted
canvess   canvas
mustache   mustash
peddaler   peddler

Word Search

Circle the fifteen state names from this week's list in the puzzle below.

```
U  B  Y  Y  A  R  K  A  N  S  A  S  Y
G  C  K  N  Q  F  S  G  A  O  H  I  O
A  M  C  A  Y  I  L  L  I  N  O  I  S
N  I  U  G  E  V  X  O  G  Z  T  I  S
A  S  T  I  T  M  S  O  R  I  O  W  A
I  S  N  H  A  E  D  Y  O  I  S  U  S
S  I  E  C  I  L  N  Z  E  T  D  W  A
I  S  K  I  D  S  A  N  G  M  E  A  S
U  S  U  M  H  G  G  B  E  O  O  U  N
O  I  X  D  N  E  B  R  A  S  K  A  A
L  P  N  P  G  S  Y  L  J  M  S  W  K
U  P  F  B  T  I  V  Y  V  F  A  E  E
Z  I  X  I  N  D  I  A  N  A  U  S  E
```

More State Names

Pretest Directions
Fold the paper in half. Use the blanks to write each word as it is said to you. When you finish the test, unfold the paper and correct any spelling mistakes. Practice those words for the Final Test.

1. _____	1. **Idaho**
2. _____	2. **Oregon**
3. _____	3. **Washington**
4. _____	4. **Wyoming**
5. _____	5. **Alaska**
6. _____	6. **California**
7. _____	7. **Colorado**
8. _____	8. **Montana**
9. _____	9. **Nevada**
10. _____	10. **Missouri**
11. _____	11. **Utah**
12. _____	12. **Arizona**
13. _____	13. **New Mexico**
14. _____	14. **Texas**
15. _____	15. **Oklahoma**

Challenge Words

Challenge Words	
_____	**afford**
_____	**permission**
_____	**thieves**
_____	**burglar**
	submitted

To Parents,
Here are the results of your child's weekly spelling Pretest. You can help your child study for the Final Test by following these simple steps for each word on the word list:
1. Read the word to your child.
2. Have your child write the word, saying each letter as it is written.
3. Say each letter of the word as your child checks the spelling.
4. If a mistake has been made, have your child read each letter of the correctly spelled word aloud, and then repeat steps 1–3.

Children who read and write at home are usually good spellers. Encourage your child to write something every day.

Parent/Child Activity:
Help your child learn state locations. First, allow your child to study a map of the United States. Then, using the map, describe where each state from this week's list is located, and see if your child can name the state. For example, for Oregon you might say, "This state is on the Pacific Coast, north of California and south of Washington."

Macmillan/McGraw-Hill

More State Names

Write the state names from the list that end with the letter *a*.

1. _____   3. _____   5. _____

2. _____   4. _____   6. _____

Write the state names from the list that end with the letter *o*.

1. _____

2. _____

3. _____

Scrambled States

Unscramble the letters to spell each state name. Then read down the boxed letters to find a secret message.

1. MOWINGY   [ ] __ __ __ __ __ __

2. REGOON   __ [ ] __ __ __ __

3. SKAALA   __ __ [ ] __ __ __

4. TAHU   __ [ ] __ __

5. DAVENA   __ [ ] __ __ __ __

6. DOCOLORA   __ __ __ [ ] __ __ __ __

7. ZOANAIR   __ __ __ __ [ ] __ __

8. FORIACALIN   __ __ __ __ __ __ __ __ __ __

9. TONSHINGWA   __ __ [ ] __ __ __ __ __ __ __

10. NANAMOT   __ __ __ [ ] __ __ __

11. DIAHO   __ __ [ ] __ __

12. STAXE   [ ] __ __ __ __

13. WEN COMIEX   __ [ ] __ __ __ __ __ __ __

14. SOUMISIR   __ __ [ ] __ __ __ __ __

15. HOMALOKA   __ __ __ __ __ __ __ __

16. _____

More State Names

For Short
Write the state name for each abbreviation.

1. OR _____   6. OK _____

2. AZ _____   7. MT _____

3. CO _____   8. ID _____

4. NM _____   9. WA _____

5. TX _____   10. MO _____

Puzzling States
Complete the puzzle with all fifteen state names from the list to find out their nicknames. Then write the correct state name on the line after each clue.

Across

1. Golden State _____

4. Show-Me State _____

6. Equality State _____

8. Centennial State _____

10. Sagebrush State _____

12. Land of the Midnight Sun _____

14. Land of Enchantment _____

15. Evergreen State _____

Down

2. Grand Canyon State _____

3. Sooner State _____

5. Beehive State _____

7. Mountain State _____

9. Spud State _____

11. Beaver State _____

13. Lone Star State _____

Level 11/Unit 4
Challenge Extension: Have students classify the Challenge Words by number of syllables, then write them out divided into syllables.

25

More State Names

Proofreading Paragraph
There are ten misspelled words (including some state names) in the paragraph below. Circle each misspelling and write the correctly spelled word above it.

The Golden Spike

Before 1850, Misouri, Arkansaw, Iowa, Texis, and Callifornia had no

railroads at all. The entire United States had less than 10,000 miles of railroad

traks. By 1860, however, that total had soared to more than 30,000 miles.

Although there were passenger trains from the beggining, the railroads' most

important role was carrying goods and materials from the citys in the East to the

new communitys on the western fronteer. In 1869, the Union Pacific and the

Central Pacific railroads were joined in Utah by the famous "golden spike." That

moment is when it became possible to travell by train all the way from the east

coast to the west coast.

Writing Activity
Write a paragraph about a cross-country train trip, real or imaginary. Describe the sights, smells, and sounds you associate with railroad travel.

_____

_____

_____

_____

_____

_____

_____

_____

More State Names

In the list below, some of this week's spelling words are misspelled. If the word is correct, write C on the line. If the word is misspelled, write the correct spelling on the line.

1. Idoho _____   11. Utah _____

2. Oregon _____   12. Arrizona _____

3. Washingtin _____   13. New Mexico _____

4. Wyomming _____   14. Texas _____

5. Aleska _____   15. Oklahhoma _____

6. California _____   afford _____

7. Colorodo _____   permision _____

8. Montanna _____   theives _____

9. Neveda _____   burglar _____

10. Missouri _____   submited _____

Circle fifteen state names from this week's list hidden in the puzzle below.

```
N  X  O  I  R  U  O  S  S  I  M  E  A
O  L  A  D  O  H  A  D  I  Y  G  M  W
T  S  M  N  A  S  O  R  E  G  O  N  C
G  C  O  E  O  R  U  G  S  H  A  O  I
N  A  N  V  H  Z  O  U  A  I  U  A  M
I  A  T  A  W  W  I  L  N  Q  T  K  X
H  K  A  D  D  Y  K  R  O  K  A  I  B
S  S  N  A  B  O  O  C  A  C  H  A  Q
A  A  A  U  W  F  Z  M  J  G  I  S  S
W  L  T  Z  I  G  J  I  I  S  S  S  A
X  A  M  L  S  P  Q  G  A  N  Y  D  X
L  M  A  Z  D  J  K  O  U  A  G  U  E
S  C  O  C  I  X  E  M  W  E  N  G  T
```

Even More State Names

Pretest Directions

Fold the paper in half. Use the blanks to write each word as it is said to you. When you finish the test, unfold the paper and correct any spelling mistakes. Practice those words for the Final Test.

To Parents,

Here are the results of your child's weekly spelling Pretest. You can help your child study for the Final Test by following these simple steps for each word on the word list:

1. Read the word to your child.
2. Have your child write the word, saying each letter as it is written.
3. Say each letter of the word as your child checks the spelling.
4. If a mistake has been made, have your child read each letter of the correctly spelled word aloud, and then repeat steps 1–3.

Children who read and write at home are usually good spellers. Encourage your child to write something every day. In addition, here is a spelling game you can play with your child.

Parent/Child Activity:
Help your child learn state capitals. Using a map, look up the capital of each state on this week's list. Then have your child make flash cards with the state name on one side and the capital on the other. Use the flash cards until he or she knows all fifteen capitals.

1. _____	1. **Massachusetts**
2. _____	2. **Connecticut**
3. _____	3. **New Hampshire**
4. _____	4. **Vermont**
5. _____	5. **Maine**
6. _____	6. **Rhode Island**
7. _____	7. **New York**
8. _____	8. **Pennsylvania**
9. _____	9. **Delaware**
10. _____	10. **New Jersey**
11. _____	11. **West Virginia**
12. _____	12. **Maryland**
13. _____	13. **Virginia**
14. _____	14. **North Carolina**
15. _____	15. **South Carolina**

Challenge Words

_____

_____

_____

_____

_____

Challenge Words

attempting

authorities

credit

patriot

reasonable

Macmillan/McGraw-Hill

Even More State Names

State Ends
Write the state names from the list that end with the letter *a*.

1. _____   4. _____

2. _____   5. _____

3. _____

Two-Word States
Write the state names from the list that are made up of two words.

1. _____   4. _____   6. _____

2. _____   5. _____   7. _____

3. _____

Scrambled Letters
Unscramble the letters to spell each state name.

1. CHUMSTASASTES   _____

2. WEN ROKY   _____

3. NECCUCTTION   _____

4. ADEALREW   _____

5. NWE PHIMREASH   _____

6. GRINIAVI   _____

7. EWN SEERJY   _____

8. IMENA   _____

9. DALNRAMY   _____

10. HODER SLAIND   _____

11. HOUTS ALAROCIN   _____

12. SLIPVANENANY   _____

13. TOMVERN   _____

14. STEW IGIRNIVA   _____

Even More State Names

On the Ocean
Using a map, write ten states from the list that border the Atlantic Ocean.

1. _____   6. _____

2. _____   7. _____

3. _____   8. _____

4. _____   9. _____

5. _____   10. _____

In the Northeast
Using a map, write the names of the New England states. One is done for you.

1. Rhode Island   4. _____

2. _____   5. _____

3. _____   6. _____

Short States
Write the state name for each abbreviation.

1. NH _____   9. RI _____

2. NJ _____   10. MD _____

3. NY _____   11. VA _____

4. MA _____   12. WV _____

5. CT _____   13. NC _____

6. VT _____   14. SC _____

7. ME _____   15. PA _____

8. DE _____

30

Level 11/Unit 4
Challenge Extension: Have students use the Challenge
Words to write a letter to a famous person in history.

85

Even More State Names

Proofreading Paragraph
There are ten errors (including misspelled state names) in the postcard below. Circle each error and write the correctly spelled word above it.

Whirlwind Tour

Dear Tonya,

    We arived in Philadelphia late Sunday night. Yesterday, we

saw the U.S. Mint, and today we're going to see the Liberty Bell

and a libary that Ben Franklin started. Tomorrow, we'll leave

Pensyllvania and drive to Cape May, New Jursey. From there,

we'll take a ferry to Delaware, and on Thursday we'll viset

Annapolis, the capital of Marylind. There, we will tour the U.S.

Navel Academy. On Friday, we'll travel to Williamsburg, Virginia.

By Sunday night, we should be back home in North Carolinna,

sleeping in our own beds.

    Whew! Just writing about it makes me tired. Yur lucky you

didn't have to take a vacation this summer.

    Your freind,

    Kelly

Tonya Smith
2 Rte. 0
City, NC 01111

Writing Activity
Write a paragraph about a state you would like to visit. Does someone you know live there? Is there something special in the state's capital city you would like to see? Does the state have historic sites or resort areas of interest to you?

_____

_____

_____

_____

Macmillan/McGraw-Hill

Even More State Names

In the list below, some of this week's spelling words are misspelled. If the word is correct, write *C* on the line. If the word is misspelled, write the correct spelling on the line.

1. Massachussetts _____
2. Conecticut _____
3. New Hampshire _____
4. Vermont _____
5. Maine _____
6. Rhoade Island _____
7. New York _____
8. Pensylvania _____
9. Dellaware _____
10. Marryland _____

11. New Jersey _____
12. West Virginnia _____
13. Virginnia _____
14. North Carolina _____
15. South Carolina _____

atempting _____
authorrities _____
credit _____
patriot _____
reasonabble _____

Fill in the blanks to form state names from this week's list. Then read down the boxed letters to find the answer to the riddle.

[ ] ___ INE   VIR ___ [ ] ___ ___ ___ ___

NEW ___ ___ [ ] ___ ___

___ ___ ___ ___ ___ [ ] ___ ___ ___ IRE

___ ___ [ ] ___ ONT

___ ___ [ ] ___ ___ ISL ___ ___ ___

___ ___ [ ] ___ VIR ___ [ ] ___ ___

SOU ___ ___ ___ ___ [ ] ___

CON ___ ___ ___ ___ [ ] ___

___ ___ [ ] ___ ___ ___ ___ ___ ___ NIA

MAS ___ ___ [ ] ___

N [ ] ___ ___ ORK   MAR ___ ___ [ ]

What three-syllable word is always mispronounced? _____

States and Neighbors

Pretest Directions

Fold the paper in half. Use the blanks to write each word as it is said to you. When you finish the test, unfold the paper and correct any spelling mistakes. Practice those words for the Final Test.

1. _____	1. **North Dakota**
2. _____	2. **Bahamas**
3. _____	3. **South Dakota**
4. _____	4. **District of Columbia**
5. _____	5. **Hawaii**
6. _____	6. **Dominican Republic**
7. _____	7. **Minnesota**
8. _____	8. **Jamaica**
9. _____	9. **Wisconsin**
10. _____	10. **Puerto Rico**
11. _____	11. **Canada**
12. _____	12. **Haiti**
13. _____	13. **Mexico**
14. _____	14. **Cuba**
15. _____	15. **Bermuda**

Challenge Words

_____

_____

_____

_____

_____

Challenge Words

overhung

entertains

expression

jutted

originate

To Parents,

Here are the results of your child's weekly spelling Pretest. You can help your child study for the Final Test by following these simple steps for each word on the word list:

1. Read the word to your child.
2. Have your child write the word, saying each letter as it is written.
3. Say each letter of the word as your child checks the spelling.
4. If a mistake has been made, have your child read each letter of the correctly spelled word aloud, and then repeat steps 1–3.

Children who read and write at home are usually good spellers. Encourage your child to write something every day. In addition, here is a spelling game you can play with your child.

Parent/Child Activity:

Help your child learn geography. Using a map, describe the location of a place from this week's list. Then ask your child to write down the name of the state, territory, or country. For example, for Hawaii you might say, "This state is made up of islands in the Pacific Ocean."

Macmillan/McGraw-Hill

States and Neighbors

Atlas at Last!
Write the place name from this week's list that you would find between each pair below if you were using an alphabetical atlas.

World Atlas

1. Belgium/Bolivia   _____

2. Italy/Japan   _____

3. Costa Rica/Denmark   _____

4. Brazil/Chile   _____

5. Lebanon/New Zealand   _____

6. Greece/Honduras   _____

7. Australia/Belgium   _____

8. Denmark/Ecuador   _____

U.S. Atlas

9. Virginia/Wyoming   _____

10. Georgia/Idaho   _____

11. South Carolina/Tennessee _____

12. North Carolina/Ohio   _____

13. Delaware/Florida   _____

14. Michigan/Mississippi   _____

15. Pennsylvania/Rhode Island _____

Scrambled Words
Unscramble the letters to spell each place name from the list.

1. SAMHABA _____   6. TOPURE COIR _____

2. DABMURE _____   7. THORN TAODAK _____

3. JACAIMA _____   8. SCWIONINS _____

4. DACAAN _____   9. NISMENOTA _____

5. COXIME _____   10. IWAIHA _____

States and Neighbors

What's the Name?
Write the state name for each abbreviation.

1. ND _____

2. MN _____

3. HI _____

4. SD _____

5. WI _____

Crossword
Complete the puzzle with ten place names from the list. Then fill in the blank after each capital city.

Across

2. Kingston, _____

6. Nassau, _____

9. Bismarck, _____

Down

1. Madison, _____

3. Ottawa, _____

4. Havana, _____

5. Pierre, _____

6. Hamilton, _____

7. Honolulu, _____

8. St. Paul, _____

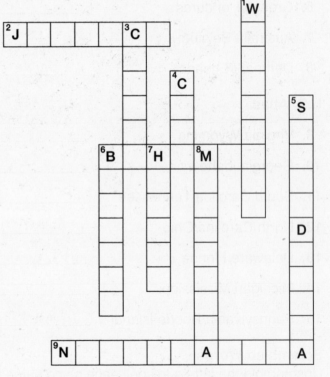

Macmillan/McGraw-Hill

Level 11/Unit 4
Challenge Extension: Have students use the Challenge Words to write a paragraph about their favorite kind of entertainment.

15

States and Neighbors

Proofreading Paragraph

Correct the ten spelling errors in the paragraph below. Circle each incorrectly spelled word and write the correctly spelled word above it.

Islands in the Sun

You might not realize it, but the United States has neighbors other than

Canada and Mexaco. Bermuta, for example, is less than five hundred miles east

of North Carolina. The Bahammas and Cuba are less than a hundred miles from

Florida. South of Cuba is Jaimaica, and east of Jamaica is an island called

Hispaniola. Hispaniola is made up of two countries, Haiti and the Dominikin

Republic. Christopher Columbis discovered all of these island neighbors except

for Bermuta. East of the Dominikin Republic is yet another island discovered by

Columbis. It is Puerto Rico, which is a commonwealth of the Unided States.

Macmillan/McGraw-Hill

States and Neighbors

In the list below, some of this week's spelling words are misspelled. If the word is correct, write *C* on the line. If the word is misspelled, circle it and write the correct spelling on the line.

1. North Dakota _____

2. South Dakota _____

3. District of Colombia

   _____

4. Hawaii _____

5. Minessota _____

6. Wisconson _____

7. Pueurto Rico _____

8. Canada _____

9. Mexico _____

10. Cuba _____

11. Haitie _____

12. Dominacon Republic

    _____

13. Jaimaica _____

14. Bahamas _____

15. Bermuta _____

    ovrhung _____

    entertains _____

    expresion _____

    jutted _____

    origanate _____

What's the Place?

Unscramble the place names. Then read down the boxed letters to find another place name from the spelling list.

COXIME _____ _____ _____ _____ [ ] _____

DAMUBER _____ _____ _____ _____ [ ] _____ _____

ASABAHM [ ] _____ _____ _____ _____ _____

THAII _____ [ ] _____ _____ _____

Solution: _____ _____ _____ _____ _____

Content Words: Animals

Pretest

1. _____   6. _____

2. _____   7. _____

3. _____   8. _____

4. _____   9. _____

5. _____   10. _____

Call Home

The animals on the word list can be found in many different places. Fill in the names of animals who would feel at home in the following environments.

farm   _____   _____

water   _____   _____

              _____   _____

frozen lands _____

Order, Please!

Can you rewrite this list in alphabetical order? Remember, if the first letters are the same, compare the second letters. If those are the same, keep going.

porpoise   _____   mustang   _____

antelope   _____   piglet   _____

penguin   _____   salamander   _____

gorilla   _____   ewe   _____

Word Journal

Write one of the list words below. Take a few minutes to write down every word that describes that animal. You might include words that tell what it looks like and why you think it is interesting. Use an encyclopedia or a reference source.

_____

_____

_____

_____

Content Words: Animals

Word List

1. beaver	5. penguin	9. antelope
2. porpoise	6. mustang	10. ewe
3. hippopotamus	7. salamander	
4. gorilla	8. piglet	

Wacky Visitors

These weird sentences all have one thing in common. If you unscramble the letters in the silly name, you'll find a list word.

Lila Rog went to Africa and saw a _____.

Stan Mug rode on a _____.

Vera Be took a bath in the lake and watched a _____.

P. T. Gile held a tiny _____.

Leona Pet went on a safari and saw an _____.

Del Armanas had a pet _____.

Guen Pin visited Antarctica and met a _____.

Proofer In Action!

No one can find what they are looking for in the book *Animals I Have Known* because all the entries in the index are misspelled. Can you correct the index? Write the correct spelling on the lines provided below.

Antellop	10, 13, 36	Mustag	12
Beever	23–25	Pangwen	19, 37
Gorila	12	Purpoise	8, 11, 15–16, 38
Hipoppotamus	34, 36, 40–41	Salemander	9–11, 16

_____

_____

_____

Review Words

Pretest

1. _____
2. _____
3. _____
4. _____
5. _____

6. _____
7. _____
8. _____
9. _____
10. _____

11. _____
12. _____
13. _____
14. _____
15. _____

Pattern Power!

Five of the list words have one spelling pattern in common. Which five are they?

_____   _____   _____

_____   _____

Straighten Up!

Rearrange these letters to form list words.

eabrve   _____   lnilislo   _____

itaHi   _____   gamtnus   _____

aanCad   _____   enpingu   _____

xsTea   _____   kAlasa   _____

omDcepuan blRiniic _____   ewN roYk   _____

Word Journal

Look at the words you wrote in **Pattern Power!** Jot down several of your favorites below. Can you think of any more words that match spelling patterns in the word list? You might work with a partner to create a list to share with your class.

_____

_____

_____

_____

_____

_____

_____

Review Words

Word List

1. Louisiana
2. penguin
3. Illinois
4. Indiana
5. Canada

6. Haiti
7. mustang
8. New York
9. North Carolina
10. Dominican Republic

11. beaver
12. Texas
13. Montana
14. Alaska
15. California

Short Division

Divide each of these words into syllables. Then write how many syllables the word has. Check your answers with your dictionary. The first one has been done for you.

pen/guin   2

Louisiana   _____

beaver   _____

Montana   _____

California   _____

Illinois   _____

Indiana   _____

mustang   _____

Proofer in Action!

Circle the five errors in this postcard. Write the correct spellings on the line below.

Dear Tyrell,

I bought a bever hat at Mardi

Gras, the festival in Lusiana.

This is the biggest party I

have ever seen. Can you   TO: Tyrell Thornton

believe I saw a pinguin on a   823 Pine Street

float? Some said it was   Addison, Illinois

from Aleska, but I know it   60101

came from the zoo in Indiena.

I'll write again soon.

    Zack

_____

Suffixes

Pretest Directions

Fold the paper in half. Use the blanks to write each word as it is said to you. When you finish the test, unfold the paper and correct any spelling mistakes. Practice those words for the Final Test.

To Parents,

Here are the results of your child's weekly spelling Pretest. You can help your child study for the Final Test by following these simple steps for each word on the word list:

1. Read the word to your child.
2. Have your child write the word, saying each letter as it is written.
3. Say each letter of the word as your child checks the spelling.
4. If a mistake has been made, have your child read each letter of the correctly spelled word aloud, and then repeat steps 1–3.

Children who read and write at home are usually good spellers. Encourage your child to write something every day. In addition, here is a spelling game you can play with your child.

Parent/Child Activity:

Many of this week's words are adjectives formed by adding the suffix -*less* or -*ful* to a noun. Examples: *helpful, helpless.* Take turns with your child to see how many -*less* words you can think of that can be turned into -*ful* words and vice versa.

1. _____	1. **colorful**
2. _____	2. **painful**
3. _____	3. **graceful**
4. _____	4. **dreadful**
5. _____	5. **hopeless**
6. _____	6. **helpful**
7. _____	7. **useless**
8. _____	8. **powerful**
9. _____	9. **wonderful**
10. _____	10. **penniless**
11. _____	11. **beautifully**
12. _____	12. **restless**
13. _____	13. **thoughtless**
14. _____	14. **thankful**
15. _____	15. **handful**

Challenge Words | **Challenge Words**

_____	**boarded**
_____	**capturing**
_____	**drought**
_____	**scratch**
_____	**bashful**

Macmillan/McGraw-Hill

Suffixes

Before the Ending

Write the list words that end with the suffix -ful in the first two columns. Write the list words that end with -less in the third column. One list word does not follow either pattern. Write that word in the fourth column. Underline the spelling pattern in each word.

-ful words   -less words

1. _____   6. _____   10. _____   15. _____

2. _____   7. _____   11. _____

3. _____   8. _____   12. _____

4. _____   9. _____   13. _____

5. _____   14. _____

What's Up, Doc?

Complete the list words below. Then read down the boxed letters to answer the riddle.

1. R _____ _____ _____ _____ _____ _____ S

2. U _____ _____ _____ _____ [_____] S

3. P _____ [_____] _____ _____ _____ L

4. H _____ _____ _____ _____ _____ L

5. C _____ _____ [_____] _____ L

WHAT DO YOU CALL A 300-POUND RABBIT? _____ _____ _____

Suffixes

Add *-ful* or *-less* to each noun to form an adjective *not* on the list. The first one is done for you.

watch   _____watchful_____

1. use _____
2. meaning _____
3. hope _____
4. worth _____
5. word _____

6. harm _____
7. spoon _____
8. joy _____
9. sleep _____
10. point _____

What's the Word?

Write the spelling word that best matches each definition below.

1. despairing _____
2. without money _____
3. elegant _____
4. vivid, bright _____
5. grateful _____
6. strong, mighty _____
7. not much, a few _____
8. very uncomfortable _____
9. useful, beneficial _____
10. fidgety, uneasy _____
11. fabulous, marvelous _____
12. unthinking, inconsiderate _____
13. awful, frightful _____
14. purposeless, unusable _____
15. attractively _____

Macmillan/McGraw-Hill

25

Level 11/Unit 5
Challenge Extension: Have students write a synonym
and an antonym for each Challenge Word.

99

Suffixes

Proofreading Paragraph

Circle the correctly spelled word in each set of parentheses in the letter below.

Dear Aaron,

I can't wait (until, untill) you come to visit. Today we got a new kitten, and we named her Lucy. Last night there was a (dreadfull, dreadful) thunderstorm, and some (thoughtless, thougtless) person left poor Lucy in front of the (animal, animall) shelter where my uncle works. At first she was very bashful and didn't want to be held. My uncle thinks that's because she had a (painful, painfull) ear infection. Now that we are giving her medication, she is recovering (beautifully, beutifully) and seems genuinely (thankful, thankfull) for having been rescued. We are keeping her in the house, but she seems a little (restles, restless) sometimes. When she is hungry, for example, she can be a real handful. This morning she jumped up on the kitchen table and knocked over my (oranje, orange) juice! She may not be the most (graseful, graceful) cat in the world, but I think you're really going to like her.

See you soon!

Your friend,

Travis

Writing Activity

Write a paragraph about an animal. You could choose to write about a pet you have or an animal you have observed in nature or at the zoo. Use at least five spelling words.

_____

_____

_____

_____

_____

_____

Suffixes

A. In the list below, some of this week's words are misspelled. If the word is correct, write *correct* on the line. If the word is misspelled, draw a line through it and write the correct spelling on the line.

1. restless _____

2. hopeless _____

3. thougtless _____

4. useless _____

5. pennyless _____

6. colorful _____

7. wunderful _____

8. beautifuly _____

9. dredful _____

10. graseful _____

11. handful _____

12. painful _____

13. helpful _____

14. powarful _____

15. thankfull _____

  borded _____

  capturing _____

  drougt _____

  scrach _____

  bashful _____

B. Use the list words to complete the crossword puzzle.

Across

5. terrible, frightful

6. grateful

8. without money

9. worthless, unusable

Down

1. aching

2. mighty

3. marvelous

4. smooth

7. fidgety

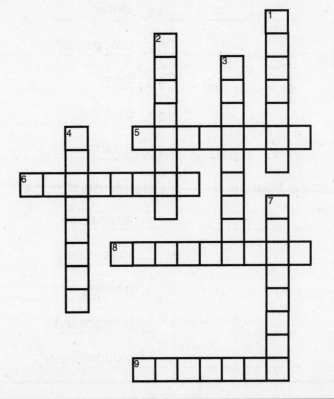

Words Ending in *or* and *er*

Pretest Directions

Fold the paper in half. Use the blanks to write each word as it is said to you. When you finish the test, unfold the paper and correct any spelling mistakes. Practice those words for the Final Test.

1. _____	1. **emperor**
2. _____	2. **whatever**
3. _____	3. **tower**
4. _____	4. **zipper**
5. _____	5. **whether**
6. _____	6. **wonder**
7. _____	7. **terror**
8. _____	8. **whenever**
9. _____	9. **odor**
10. _____	10. **meteor**
11. _____	11. **writer**
12. _____	12. **prospector**
13. _____	13. **razor**
14. _____	14. **trailer**
15. _____	15. **wherever**

Challenge Words

Challenge Words	**Challenge Words**
_____	**advantage**
_____	**assembled**
_____	**poverty**
_____	**guaranteed**
_____	**millionaire**

To Parents,

Here are the results of your child's weekly spelling Pretest. You can help your child study for the Final Test by following these simple steps for each word on the word list:

1. Read the word to your child.
2. Have your child write the word, saying each letter as it is written.
3. Say each letter of the word as your child checks the spelling.
4. If a mistake has been made, have your child read each letter of the correctly spelled word aloud, and then repeat steps 1–3.

Children who read and write at home are usually good spellers. Encourage your child to write something every day. In addition, here is a spelling game you can play with your child.

Parent/Child Activity:
Work with your child on a story using as many of the list words as possible. When you are finished, "publish" the story by sharing it with other family members or friends, either by letting them read it or by reading it aloud.

Macmillan/McGraw-Hill

Words Ending in *or* and *er*

Happy Ending

Write the words ending with *er* in the first column. Write the words ending with *or* in the second column. Underline the spelling pattern in each word.

-er words

1. _____
2. _____
3. _____
4. _____
5. _____
6. _____
7. _____
8. _____
9. _____

-or words

10. _____
11. _____
12. _____
13. _____
14. _____
15. _____

What's That Sound?

Write the list word for each phonetic respelling.

1. /ō´ dər/ _____
2. /rī´ tər/ _____
3. /hwot ev´ ər/ _____
4. /pros´ pek tər/ _____
5. /mē tē´ ər/ _____
6. /wun´ dər/ _____
7. /hwen ev´ ər/ _____
8. /ter´ ər/ _____

9. /em´ pər ər/ _____
10. /hweth´ ər/ _____
11. /tou´ ər/ _____
12. /rā´ zər/ _____
13. /zip´ ər/ _____
14. /hwer ev´ ər/ _____
15. /trā´ lər/ _____

Words Ending in *or* and *er*

Finish the Sentnce
Write the list word that best completes each sentence.

1. Perry's father pulled the boat with a _____.

2. After we made soup, the _____ of onions lingered in the house.

3. I _____ whether Jules will join the new soccer club.

4. Please review a book by your favorite _____.

5. Please let me know by Friday _____ you will be able to attend the party.

6. The new movie is about a _____ who finds gold in Alaska.

7. You are welcome to sit _____ you like.

8. Bring _____ kind of cookies you like to the bake sale.

9. From the _____, we could see for miles in every direction.

10. The first time Casey wore her new jacket, the _____ got stuck.

11. Miguel's aunt had a _____ of mice.

12. This knife is as sharp as a _____.

13. We went outside at ten o'clock to watch the _____ shower.

14. Hans Christian Andersen wrote a story about a vain _____.

Word Match
Write the list word that most closely matches each definition.

1. ruler _____

2. goldseeker _____

3. clothing fastener _____

4. fright _____

5. amazement _____

6. author _____

7. if _____

8. no matter when _____

9. sharp blade _____

10. tall structure _____

11. any place _____

12. wagon or cart _____

13. shooting star _____

14. smell _____

Challenge Extension: Have students use the Challenge Words in a paragraph that tells what they would do if they won a million dollars.

Level 11/Unit 5

28

Macmillan/McGraw-Hill

Words Ending in *or* and *er*

Proofreading Paragraph
Circle the correctly spelled word in each set of parentheses.

Other Worlds

August 16

   (Whenever, Wenever) I get a chance to stargaze, I always (wunder, wonder) if there is life on other planets. I also like to make up my own constellations. One of my favorites I call the (emperer, emperor). Before last night, I had never seen a shooting star. In the city where we live, there are so many (bright, brite) lights that it is hard to see any stars. Now I have seen dozens of shooting stars, because last night Dad took me to his (friend's, freind's) farm to watch (metier, meteor) showers. The farther away from the city we got, the more stars became (visible, vizible). Dad parked the car next to a (cornfeild, cornfield) and we sat on the hood, alone with the sounds of crickets and the (oder, odor) of the wet earth. (Wherever, Warever) I looked in the sky, there was a shooting star. It was better than fireworks.

Writing Activity
What do you think about when you look up at the night sky? Do you wonder what it would be like to travel in space or walk on the moon? Write a paragraph, using at least two list words.

_____

_____

_____

_____

_____

_____

_____

_____

Words Ending in *or* and *er*

One word in each set is spelled correctly. Underline the correctly spelled word and write it on the line.

1. prosspector
prospector
prospecter

_____

6. emperor
emporor
emperer

11. wearever
wherever
werever

advantadge
advantidge
advantage

_____

2. tearor
teror
terror

_____

7. ziper
zippor
zipper

12. whatever
wahtever
whatevor

assembled
asembled
assembbled

_____

3. razor
rasor
razer

_____

8. writter
writer
riter

13. whenevo
whenever
wenever

povorty
povertie
poverty

_____

4. oder
odur
odor

_____

9. wondor
wunder
wonder

14. towwer
towor
tower

garenteed
guaranteed
guarantied

_____

5. meteor
metier
meteore

10. wheather
wether
whether

15. trailor
trailler
trailer

milionairre
millionairre
millionaire

_____

Prefixes

Pretest Directions

Fold the paper in half. Use the blanks to write each word as it is said to you. When you finish the test, unfold the paper and correct any spelling mistakes. Practice those words for the Final Test.

To Parents,

   Here are the results of your child's weekly spelling Pretest. You can help your child study for the Final Test by following these simple steps for each word on the word list:

1. Read the word to your child.
2. Have your child write the word, saying each letter as it is written.
3. Say each letter of the word as your child checks the spelling.
4. If a mistake has been made, have your child read each letter of the correctly spelled word aloud, and then repeat steps 1–3.
   Children who read and write at home are usually good spellers. Encourage your child to write something every day. In addition, here is a spelling game you can play with your child.

Parent/Child Activity:

Set a timer for five minutes, and see how many words your child can write down that start with the prefix *dis*. Set the timer for five more minutes, and do the same for the suffix *pre*, then again for *sub*.

1. _____	1. **disease**
2. _____	2. **preview**
3. _____	3. **submarine**
4. _____	4. **prehistoric**
5. _____	5. **prefix**
6. _____	6. **prepaid**
7. _____	7. **disagree**
8. _____	8. **subterranean**
9. _____	9. **discourage**
10. _____	10. **discount**
11. _____	11. **preschool**
12. _____	12. **disaster**
13. _____	13. **disapprove**
14. _____	14. **subway**
15. _____	15. **pretest**

Challenge Words   **Challenge Words**

_____   **admission**

_____   **gigantic**

_____   **reptile**

_____   **specimen**

_____   **patio**

Prefixes

Pattern Power!

Write the list words that start with the prefix *dis* in the first column, the list words that start with *pre* in the second column, and the list words that start with the prefix *sub* in the third column. Underline the prefix in each word.

dis	*pre*	*sub*
1. _____	7. _____	13. _____
2. _____	8. _____	14. _____
3. _____	9. _____	15. _____
4. _____	10. _____	
5. _____	11. _____	
6. _____	12. _____	

Riddle Me This

Complete the list words below. Then unscramble the boxed letters to answer the riddle.

1. SU[B]_____ _____ _____

2. SU[B]_____ _____ _____ _____ _____

3. SUB _____ _____ _____ [____] _____ _____ _____

4. DIS[____]G _____ _____ _____

5. DIS[____]_____ _____ V _____

6. DIS _____ _____ _____ _____ [____]G _____

7. [P]RE _____ _____ _____ W

8. PRE _____ _____ [____]T

9. PRE _____ _____ _____ [____]L

10. PRE[____]_____ _____ _____ _____ _____ _____ C

WHERE DO SHEEP GET THEIR HAIR CUT?

AT THE _____ _____ _____ _____ _____ _____ _____ _____ _____

Macmillan/McGraw-Hill

Prefixes

Word Definitions
Write the list word that matches each definition.

1. catastrophe _____

2. illness _____

3. ancient _____

4. underwater ship _____

5. underground _____

6. underground train _____

7. look ahead _____

8. paid ahead _____

9. a lower price _____

10. contradict or argue _____

Fill in the Blanks
Write the list word that best completes each sentence.

1. My sister and I usually _____ about which movie to see.

2. José's father takes the _____ to his job in Manhattan.

3. The fourth graders volunteered to help in the _____.

4. The huge cave with its many wonders is a true _____ marvel.

5. Before our math test each week, we have a _____.

6. This toy _____ really goes underwater.

7. Most amusement parks offer a _____ for large groups.

8. Anna's first attempt at baking a cake was a _____.

9. The words *disturb*, *disaster*, and *discount* all have the same _____.

10. At the museum, the class saw fossils of _____ sea animals.

Macmillan/McGraw-Hill

20

Level 11/Unit 5
Challenge Extension: Have students use the Challenge Words to
write a paragraph telling about a visit to a museum or zoo.

109

Prefixes

Proofreading Paragraph
There are ten misspelled words in the letter below. Circle each misspelling and write the correctly spelled word on the lines below the paragraph.

World Down Under

Dear Uncle Mike,

Thanks for the birthday present. My friend Kim and I used the prepayed movie tickets to see a new science fiction film. Kim had discont coupons for popcorn at the same theater, so it worked out well. The movie was about cave creatures that have been living in an unknown subterannean world for thousands of years. Scientists in a submarene discovur an underwater cave that leeds to the creatures' preehistoric world. The creatures are friendly and not dangerous at all, but the scientists accidentally bring about a dizaster by introducing new germs to the creatures. When the creatures start dying of a mysterious diseese, the scientists try hard to prevent their extinction, but it is too late. It was a grate movie. Thanks again!

Your niece,

Hannah

_____

_____

Writing Activity
Write a paragraph about a movie you have seen. Use at least one word with the prefix *dis* and one word with the prefix *pre*.

_____

_____

_____

_____

Prefixes

Which is Correct?

In the list below, some of this week's words are misspelled. If the word is correct, write *correct* on the line. If the word is misspelled, write the correct spelling on the line.

1. disaster _____
2. disaggree _____
3. disaprove _____
4. discorage _____
5. discount _____
6. disease _____
7. prehistoraic _____
8. preschool _____
9. prepayed _____
10. prefix _____
11. pretest _____
12. preveiw _____
13. subterannean _____
14. submarine _____
15. subway _____
   admision _____
   gigantic _____
   reptile _____
   specimin _____
   pattio _____

Scrambled Words

Unscramble the list words. Then read down the boxed letters to find another list word.

1. SEADISE   [ ] ___ ___ ___ ___ ___
2. AGEDRISE   ___ [ ] ___ ___ ___ ___ ___
3. SWAUBY   [ ] ___ ___ ___ ___ ___
4. LOOPCRESH   ___ ___ ___ [ ] ___ ___ ___ ___
5. TRESIADS   ___ ___ ___ ___ ___ ___ ___ ___
6. RICHIRESTOP   ___ ___ ___ ___ ___ ___ ___ [ ] ___ ___
7. CODISURAGE   ___ ___ ___ ___ [ ] ___ ___ ___ ___
8. WEVIPRE   ___ ___ ___ ___ ___ ___ ___
9. RANETERBUSAN   ___ ___ ___ ___ ___ ___ ___ ___ ___ [ ] ___ ___
10. STREEPT   ___ ___ ___ ___ [ ] ___ ___

SOLUTION: ___ ___ ___ ___ ___ ___ ___ ___ ___ ___

Words Often Misspelled

Pretest Directions
Fold the paper in half. Use the blanks to write each word as it is said to you. When you ·
finish the test, unfold the paper and correct any spelling mistakes. Practice those words for
the Final Test.

1. _____	1. **fierce** _____
2. _____	2. **salmon** _____
3. _____	3. **weigh** _____
4. _____	4. **business** _____
5. _____	5. **theater** _____
6. _____	6. **frighten** _____
7. _____	7. **asking** _____
8. _____	8. **dealt** _____
9. _____	9. **magazine** _____
10. _____	10. **debt** _____
11. _____	11. **fourteen** _____
12. _____	12. **sandwich** _____
13. _____	13. **prisoner** _____
14. _____	14. **ocean** _____
15. _____	15. **piano** _____

Challenge Words

Challenge Words

_____   **arrested**

_____   **pelted**

_____   **persuade**

_____   **register**

_____   **stained**

To Parents,
Here are the results of your child's weekly spelling Pretest. You can help your child study for the Final Test by following these simple steps for each word on the word list:
1. Read the word to your child.
2. Have your child write the word, saying each letter as it is written.
3. Say each letter of the word as your child checks the spelling.
4. If a mistake has been made, have your child read each letter of the correctly spelled word aloud, and then repeat steps 1–3.
Children who read and write at home are usually good spellers. Encourage your child to write something every day. In addition, here is a spelling game you can play with your child.

Parent/Child Activity:
Ask your child to write words that are difficult to spell, such as those on this list. Put them in a box or basket. Once a month or so, ask your child to draw cards randomly from the box for a written quiz. After your child spells the word correctly on several quizzes, "retire" that word.

Macmillan/McGraw-Hill

Words Often Misspelled

Sound It Out
Write the list word for each phonetic spelling.

1. /wā/ _____
2. /saˊ mən/ _____
3. /bizˊ nis/ _____
4. /thēˊ ə tər/ _____
5. /fôrˊ tēn/ _____

6. /prizˊ ə nər/ _____
7. /pē anˊ ō/ _____
8. /det/ _____
9. /oˊ shən/ _____
10. /fîrs/ _____

Look It Up!
Write the list word you would find between each pair of words in a dictionary.

1. mad / magnify _____
2. print / problem _____
3. article / atlas _____
4. thaw / thief _____
5. weekly / weird _____

6. fidget / finger _____
7. death / decide _____
8. frame / fuel _____
9. sailboat / salty _____
10. physical / pickle _____

A Fishy Riddle
Complete the list words. Then read down the boxed letters to answer the riddle.

1. FR☐ ___ ___ ___ EN
2. O ___ ___ ___ ☐
3. F ___ ___ ___ ___ ___ ___
4. ___ ☐ ___ ING
5. SAND ___ ___ ☐ ___
6. W ___ ___ ___ ☐
7. P ___ ___ ___ ☐
8. ___ ☐ ___ ___ TEEN
9. ___ ___ ☐ MON
10. ___ ___ ___ ☐ ___ ___ ER

WHY ARE SALMON SO SMART? THEY SWIM _____.

Words Often Misspelled

Replaceable Words
Write the list word that can replace the underlined word or words in each sentence.

1. The child was afraid of the cartoon about a <u>ferocious</u> lion. _____

2. We need to <u>consider</u> the advantages and disadvantages of each plan. _____

3. The movie had already started when we arrived at the <u>cinema</u>. _____

4. This camera takes pictures at the bottom of the <u>sea</u>. _____

5. Kyle taught himself how to play the <u>keyboard</u>. _____

6. There are <u>more than a dozen</u> new students this year. _____

7. Most of the customers were <u>inquiring</u> about the store's new hours. _____

8. Tend to your own <u>affairs</u>. _____

9. The deep snow made her feel like a <u>captive</u> in the house. _____

10. I need to repay a five-dollar <u>loan</u>. _____

Follow the Clues
Write the list word that fits each clue. Then fill in the numbered blanks below to find the name of a popular summer activity.

1. light meal _____ _____ _____ _____ _____ _____ _____ _____
   3

2. type of fish _____ _____ _____ _____ _____ _____

3. scare _____ _____ _____ _____ _____ _____ _____
   4

4. requesting _____ _____ _____ _____ _____
   5

5. seven plus seven _____ _____ _____ _____ _____ _____ _____ _____
   1   6

6. put on a scale _____ _____ _____ _____ _____
   7

7. jailed person _____ _____ _____ _____ _____ _____ _____ _____ _____
   2

8. handed out _____ _____ _____ _____

SOLUTION: _____ _____ _____ _____ _____ _____ _____
          1   2   3   4   5   6   7

Level 11/Unit 5
Challenge Extension: Have students write a short news item
that includes as many of the Challenge Words as possible.
18

Macmillan/McGraw-Hill

Words Often Misspelled

Proofreading Paragraph
Circle the correctly spelled word in each set of parentheses.

Natives of the Forty-Ninth State

To a visitor just (arriving, ariving) in Alaska, our largest state may appear nearly

unpopulated. A closer look, however, will (reveal, reveel) many inhabitants, although not all

of these are human. Animals native to Alaska include caribou, (artic, arctic) foxes, wolves,

sea otters, eagles, and grizzly bears. One of the largest native Alaskans is the polar bear.

An (especialy, especially) large polar bear can stand more than ten feet tall and (weigh, way)

nearly a ton. Black bears are also a common sight in Alaska, but they are not nearly as

(fierce, feirce) as (poler, polar) bears. While polar bears (prefer, preffer) to eat large

mammals such as (seels, seals), black bears are happy fishing for (samon, salmon) in

Alaska's icy streams.

Writing Activity
Write a paragraph about bears. How much do you really know about them? Is there
anything you have always wondered about bears? How would you go about finding the
answers to your questions? Try to include words from the spelling list.

_____

_____

_____

_____

_____

_____

_____

Macmillan/McGraw-Hill

Words Often Misspelled

One word in each set is spelled correctly. Write the correctly spelled word on the line.

1. feirce
fierse
fierce
feerce

_____

2. delt
deallt
dealed
dealt

_____

3. debt
det
debbt
detbt

_____

4. samon
salman
salmond
salmon

_____

5. weigh
wegh
weih
waigh

_____

6. busines
business
bizness
bussiness

_____

7. theatue
theater
theiter
theeater

_____

8. friten
frightn
frighten
freighten

_____

9. askeng
aksing
asking
askin

_____

10. fourteen
forteen
fourtene
fourtteen

_____

11. sandwhich
sandwich
sandwitch
saindwich

_____

12. prisonor
prisoner
prizener
prisonner

_____

13. ochean
oshean
oceon
ocean

_____

14. pianno
peano
piano
piana

_____

15. maggazine
magazene
magazin
magazine

_____

arrested
arested
arrestted
arrestid

_____

pellted
peltid
peltted
pelted

_____

persuede
persuade
persuaid
pursuade

_____

registir
register
reggister
regester

_____

staned
stayned
stained
stainned

_____

Macmillan/McGraw-Hill

Content Words: Things You Wear

Pretest

1. _____   6. _____

2. _____   7. _____

3. _____   8. _____

4. _____   9. _____

5. _____   10. _____

Pattern Power!

Find two list words that contain each of the following smaller words. There are six blanks to fill in, but only five list words are needed. One of them is used twice!

glass _____   _____

over _____   _____

coat _____   _____

Fashion Sense

Write in the list words for clothing and accessories that someone would wear for each of the occasions below. You can start off by filling in clothing that would be appropriate anytime.

anytime _____   first day of school _____

picnic on the beach _____   house painting _____

Word Journal

Notice that the list words are all things to wear. Pretend you are going away on a vacation. Decide what items you would pack to take with you. Using as many of the list words as you can, write the items below.

_____

_____

_____

_____

_____

_____

Content Words: Things You Wear

Word List

1. T-shirt
2. overalls
3. parka
4. eyeglasses

5. necktie
6. overcoat
7. wristwatch

8. sunglasses
9. raincoat
10. jewelry

Straighten Up!
Rearrange these letter jumbles to form list words.

wejrely _____

akarp _____

slassuseng _____

thratwicws _____

Finish the Job
Fill in the blanks using list words to complete these sentences.

The sudden shower made Helen wish she had worn a _____.

In the winter, Evan wore a sweatshirt with a _____ underneath.

My _____ have helped my vision.

I'd rather wear _____ than regular pants.

The new _____ kept good time.

I have to learn how to tie a _____.

Proofer in Action!
Can you correct the spelling errors in this garage sale sign? Circle the five misspelled words and write the correct spelling on the line provided.

USED CLOTHING AND ACCESSORIES

EXCELLENT CONDITION!!!

Silk nectye 99¢

100% Wool overcote $ 15

Songlasses 75¢

Cotton T-Shurt $3

Costume jelewry— assorted prices

_____

Review Words

Pretest

1. _____ 6. _____ 11. _____

2. _____ 7. _____ 12. _____

3. _____ 8. _____ 13. _____

4. _____ 9. _____ 14. _____

5. _____ 10. _____ 15. _____

Pattern Power!

Write the list words that fit these spelling patterns.

_____ _____ _____ _____ _____ _____ e r

_____ _____ _____ _____ e r

_____ _____ _____ e r

_____ _____ _____ _____ _____ f u l

_____ _____ _____ _____ _____ f u l

m _____ _____ _____ o _____

_____ _____ n d _____ _____ _____ _____

One of Three

Each statement below is true, false, or an opinion. An opinion is based on belief, so it can't be true or false. Write *True*, *False*, or *Opinion* to classify each statement.

_____ Every list word is an adjective.

_____ *Prehistoric* is the most interesting word on the list.

_____ One list word has five syllables.

_____ The most useful word in the list is *thankful*.

_____ The hardest list word to spell is *sandwich*.

_____ There are no prepositions on the word list.

_____ The word *submarine* has four syllables.

_____ One word on the list rhymes with *pet*.

Review Words

Word List

1. colorful
2. overcoat
3. sunglasses
4. thankful
5. jewelry
6. submarine
7. disaster
8. restless
9. debt
10. prehistoric
11. meteor
12. tower
13. wonder
14. sandwich
15. ocean

Mumbo Jumble

Rearrange each group of letters to find a list word. Write each word at the right. Then rearrange the circled letters to spell a hidden word.

rywjeel _____

mesbirnau _____

nuessslags _____

klutnahf _____

wotre _____

Solution: _____

Proofer in Action!

This movie theater is showing five new movies. Can you fix the spelling mistakes in the titles? Circle the misspelled words and write the correct spellings on the line below.

The Ghost in the Touer

Night of the Meeteor

Ressless Hearts

Disastor Zone 2

The Crocodile in the Green Overcote

_____

What do you think each movie would be like? Which would you want to see?

_____

_____

Words Trusty and Doubtful

Pretest Directions

Fold the paper in half. Use the blanks to write each word as it is said to you. When you finish the test, unfold the paper and correct any spelling mistakes. Practice those words for the Final Test.

To Parents,

Here are the results of your child's weekly spelling Pretest. You can help your child study for the Final Test by following these simple steps for each word on the word list:

1. Read the word to your child.
2. Have your child write the word, saying each letter as it is written.
3. Say each letter of the word as your child checks the spelling.
4. If a mistake has been made, have your child read each letter of the correctly spelled word aloud, and then repeat steps 1–3.

Children who read and write at home are usually good spellers. Encourage your child to write something every day. In addition, here is a spelling game you can play with your child.

Parent/Child Activity:

Show your child the word *depend* within the list word *dependable* and have him or her write both words. Then look for words within the other spelling words.

1. _____	1. reliable
2. _____	2. trustworthy
3. _____	3. doubtful
4. _____	4. dubious
5. _____	5. suspicious
6. _____	6. dependable
7. _____	7. false
8. _____	8. discomfort
9. _____	9. error
10. _____	10. misleading
11. _____	11. uneasy
12. _____	12. watchful
13. _____	13. truthful
14. _____	14. actual
15. _____	15. prove

Challenge Words	**Challenge Words**
_____	observations
_____	swerved
_____	automatically
_____	incorrectly
_____	skeptical

Macmillan/McGraw-Hill

Words Trusty and Doubtful

In the Dictionary
Write the list word you would find between each pair of words in a dictionary.

1. departure/deposit _____
2. miserable/mistaken _____
3. release/relief _____
4. faithful/famous _____
5. disclose/disconnect _____
6. troublesome/truthful _____
7. erratic/erupt _____
8. watchdog/water _____

9. double/dough _____
10. unearth/unless _____
11. trusty/try _____
12. dry/duck _____
13. actress/again _____
14. proud/provide _____
15. suspense/swallow _____

What's the Word?
Write the list word or words that follow each spelling pattern. Underline the pattern in each word you write. (One word will be used twice.)

mis-   1. _____

-ful   2. _____

         3. _____

         4. _____

-dis   5. _____

-able   6. _____

         7. _____

-ing   8. _____

-ous   9. _____

         10. _____

Macmillan/McGraw-Hill

Words Trusty and Doubtful

Word Sort

This week's list contains a number of adjectives, some with positive connotations and some negative. Sort the boxed words into the correct columns below.

reliable	trustworthy	doubtful	dubious	suspicious
false	misleading	truthful	loyal	dependable

Positive adjectives

1. _____

2. _____

3. _____

4. _____

5. _____

Negative adjectives

6. _____

7. _____

8. _____

9. _____

10. _____

Crossword

Write a list word for each clue. (Note: Many of the list words are synonyms.)

Across

3. uncertain
5. honest
8. verify
10. dependable
11. alert
12. untrue
13. deceptive

Down

1. uneasiness
2. honorable
3. uncertain
4. questionable
6. real
7. reliable
9. mistake

25

Level 11/Unit 6
Challenge Extension: Ask students to use the Challenge
Words in a description of a traffic accident.

123

Words Trusty and Doubtful

Proofreading Paragraph
Underline each incorrectly spelled word and write the correctly spelled word on the lines that follow. You should find ten misspellings.

Dog's Best Friend

When you get a new puppy, it is importint to remember that bad habits can be hard to brake. You may see nothing wrong with a ten-pound puppy jumping up on your legs, but that puppy won't be little forever. That particular bad habit could prove harmfull if your dog knocks down one of your friends someday. If you want to be sure that your dog develops into a relyable and trust-worthy companion, you'll need to be a dependible pet owner. Dogs need more than food, water, and exercize. They also need clear limits. You might consider teaching your puppy a few simple comands such as "come," "stay," and "heel." And allways be sure to pronounce the commands clearly so they are not misleding.

_____

_____

Writing Activity
Write a paragraph about a pet you know. Is it well-behaved, loyal, or affectionate? Try to use at least two list words.

_____

_____

_____

_____

_____

_____

_____

_____

Words Trusty and Doubtful

In the list below, some of this week's spelling words are misspelled. If a word is correct, write *C* on the line. If a word is misspelled, write the correct spelling on the line.

1. reliable _____
2. trustwurthy _____
3. doubtfull _____
4. dubius _____
5. suspicious _____
6. dependible _____
7. false _____
8. actuel _____
9. watchful _____
10. misleding _____

11. pruve _____
12. discomfort _____
13. truthfull _____
14. loyal _____
15. uneasy _____
    obserrvations _____
    swurved _____
    autamatically _____
    incorectly _____
    sceptical _____

Scrambled Words

Unscramble the list words below. Then unscramble the boxed letters to find another list word.

1. LWUACHFT ___ ___ ___ [___] ___ ___ ___ ___
2. SLEAF ___ ___ [___] ___ ___
3. DEAMISLING ___ ___ [___] ___ ___ ___ ___ ___ ___
4. TRIMFOOCSD ___ [___] ___ ___ ___ ___ ___ ___ ___
5. BLEPENDADE ___ ___ [___] ___ ___ ___ ___ ___ ___
6. WORRYTHTUST ___ ___ [___] ___ ___ ___ ___ ___ ___ ___ ___
7. FLUTODUB ___ ___ [___] ___ ___ ___ ___ ___
8. ERVOP ___ ___ [___] ___ ___
9. IAREELBL ___ ___ ___ [___] ___ ___ ___ ___
10. SUBUDIO ___ ___ ___ ___ [___] ___ ___

UNSCRAMBLED WORD: ___ ___ ___ ___ ___ ___ ___ ___ ___ ___

Past-Tense Endings

Pretest Directions
Fold the paper in half. Use the blanks to write each word as it is said to you. When you finish the test, unfold the paper and correct any spelling mistakes. Practice those words for the Final Test.

1. _____	1. revealed
2. _____	2. concealed
3. _____	3. heaved
4. _____	4. peeked
5. _____	5. chortled
6. _____	6. slandered
7. _____	7. flaked
8. _____	8. controlled
9. _____	9. worshiped
10. _____	10. traveled
11. _____	11. uncharted
12. _____	12. walked
13. _____	13. amused
14. _____	14. thanked
15. _____	15. resisted

Challenge Words

Challenge Words	Challenge Words
_____	strides
_____	attract
_____	markings
_____	digesting
_____	nimble

To Parents,
Here are the results of your child's weekly spelling Pretest. You can help your child study for the Final Test by following these simple steps for each word on the word list:
1. Read the word to your child.
2. Have your child write the word, saying each letter as it is written.
3. Say each letter of the word as your child checks the spelling.
4. If a mistake has been made, have your child read each letter of the correctly spelled word aloud, and then repeat steps 1–3.

Children who read and write at home are usually good spellers. Encourage your child to write something every day.

Parent/Child Activity:
Set a timer for five minutes. See how many other verbs that form the past tense by adding -ed you and your child can think of. It's fun to play in teams, too.

Past-Tense Endings

Pattern Power!
Write the list word or words that follow each pattern. Underline the pattern in each word.

-red 1. _____ *-lled* 5. _____

-sed 2. _____ *-ped* 6. _____

-ted 3. _____ *-tled* 7. _____

4. _____ *-ealed* 8. _____

In the Past
Write the past tense of each verb below. The even-numbered words are not from your list, but they share some spelling patterns with the list words next to them.

1. worship _____ 2. gossip _____

3. reveal _____ 4. heal _____

5. thank _____ 6. honk _____

7. flake _____ 8. quake _____

9. amuse _____ 10. tease _____

11. heave _____ 12. shove _____

13. peek _____ 14. leak _____

15. conceal _____ 16. repeal _____

17. chortle _____ 18. hurtle _____

Look It Up!
Write the list word you would find alphabetized between each pair of words in a dictionary.

1. skyscraper / slang _____

2. repaid / repeated _____

3. hurried / husband _____

4. amount / anchor _____

Past-Tense Endings

Word Match
Write the list word that most closely matches each word or phrase below.

1. opposed _____
2. strolled _____
3. laughed _____
4. disclosed _____
5. hid _____
6. defamed _____
7. peeled _____
8. expressed gratitude _____

9. entertained _____
10. lifted _____
11. took a trip _____
12. looked _____
13. adored _____
14. regulated _____
15. unmapped _____

Finish the Sentence
Write the list word that best completes each sentence.

1. Carlos _____ around the corner to see who was honking.

2. The class was _____ by the mime's performance.

3. The dog _____ all of my efforts to get him in the car.

4. She _____ the model airplane with a battery-powered device.

5. Mrs. Kritzer _____ us for raking her leaves.

6. We _____ the last bag of old clothes into the truck.

7. Mike's brother _____ with us to Mexico last summer.

8. Jennifer _____ at the principal's joke.

9. The stain on his tie was _____ by his jacket.

10. Kayla _____ up the street to her sister's house.

Level 11/Unit 6
Challenge Extension: Have students use the
Challenge Words to write a one-page story.

25

Past-Tense Endings

Proofreading Paragraph
For each pair of words in parentheses, underline the correctly spelled word.

Thank You, Mr. Edison

No other person in (history, historie) has (inventted, invented) more useful

things than Thomas Edison. As a boy, Edison (amused, amuzed) himself with

electrical experiments and started tinkering with (telegraff, telegraph)

equipment. When he was twenty-one, Edison (turnned, turned) to inventing full

time. Thomas Edison can (certainly, certinly) be thanked for making our daily

lives (easier, eazier). To appreciate what Edison did, just try to imagine life

without telephones or electric (lites, lights). Edison also invented the

phonograph, and other inventors who worked in his laboratory (helped, helpped)

to (davelop, develop) motion pictures. If it weren't for Thomas Edison, we might

not have stereos, televisions, or computers.

Writing Activity
Many items you probably use every day were not around when your parents were young.
Write a paragraph describing what you think a typical day was like for your parents or
grandparents when they were your age.

_____

_____

_____

_____

_____

Past-Tense Endings

One word in each pair is spelled correctly and one incorrectly. Write the correctly spelled word on the line.

1. revaled   revealed   _____
2. concealed   conceled   _____
3. heaved   heived   _____
4. peeked   peiked   _____
5. chorteled   chortled   _____
6. slanderred   slandered   _____
7. flakked   flaked   _____
8. controlled   controled   _____
9. worshippd   worshiped   _____
10. travled   traveled   _____

11. uncharded   uncharted   _____
12. wolked   walked   _____
13. amused   amuzed   _____
14. thanked   thainked   _____
15. rezisted   resisted   _____
    strides   strieds   _____
    attract   atract   _____
    markkings   markings   _____
    dijesting   digesting   _____
    nimbble   nimble   _____

All twenty of the list words are hidden in the puzzles below. Circle each one you find.

```
P W U O C H O R T L E D        W D U E D E T S I S E R X
M R D G K H D F G Y G W        A R D L T X B B Z Z M T A
Q P E Q A I E L K K S O        L J Z B J R B K U F C G M
V S L D P Y L A F H L R        K O M M M K Z N F A R N U
M Q L E E S A K V T A S        E N M I H P C T R H X I S
I F O L E T E E X E N H        D A E N K H S T D M D T E
S I R A K A C D L Y D I        Z E E V A T T E A E N S D
P S T E E R N I P E E P        U X H R R A T R K M B E S
W D N V D T O J P O R E        T Z T I I S K N J A X G A
S D O E Z L C D C K E D        O E D E I I A K K N N I I
F E C R H E B S M I D F        D E M S N H C B G P M D X
F Y E X A D T E U I J B        S F N G T A J A Z V T E O
                               V I S X U D E L E V A R T
```

Science Words

Pretest Directions

Fold the paper in half. Use the blanks to write each word as it is said to you. When you finish the test, unfold the paper and correct any spelling mistakes. Practice those words for the Final Test.

To Parents,

Here are the results of your child's weekly spelling Pretest. You can help your child study for the Final Test by following these simple steps for each word on the word list:

1. Read the word to your child.
2. Have your child write the word, saying each letter as it is written.
3. Say each letter of the word as your child checks the spelling.
4. If a mistake has been made, have your child read each letter of the correctly spelled word aloud, and then repeat steps 1–3.

Children who read and write at home are usually good spellers. Encourage your child to write something every day.

Parent/Child Activity:

Ask your child to choose five list words. Then ask him or her to see how many words can be spelled using the letters from each word. For example, the letters in the word *atomic* can be used to spell *cat*, *coat*, and so on.

1. _____	1. scientist
2. _____	2. scientific
3. _____	3. procedure
4. _____	4. experiment
5. _____	5. test tube
6. _____	6. microscope
7. _____	7. curious
8. _____	8. careful
9. _____	9. serious
10. _____	10. molecule
11. _____	11. atoms
12. _____	12. atomic
13. _____	13. molecular
14. _____	14. method
15. _____	15. methodical

Challenge Words   **Challenge Words**

_____   concentrated

_____   gravity

_____   microscopic

_____   reduced

_____   rival

Science Words

Common Roots
Write the list words in alphabetical order. Which four pairs of words share a root?

1. _____   5. _____   9. _____   13. _____

2. _____   6. _____   10. _____   14. _____

3. _____   7. _____   11. _____   15. _____

4. _____   8. _____   12. _____

Words that share a root: _____ and _____;

_____ and _____; _____ and

_____; and _____ and _____

Noun or Not?
Write all the list words that are nouns in the first two columns and all the list words that are adjectives in the second two columns.

<table>
<tr><td colspan="2" align="center">nouns</td><td colspan="2" align="center">adjectives</td></tr>
<tr><td>1. _____</td><td>5. _____</td><td>9. _____</td><td>13. _____</td></tr>
<tr><td>2. _____</td><td>6. _____</td><td>10. _____</td><td>14. _____</td></tr>
<tr><td>3. _____</td><td>7. _____</td><td>11. _____</td><td>15. _____</td></tr>
<tr><td>4. _____</td><td>8. _____</td><td>12. _____</td><td></td></tr>
</table>

Complete the list words. Then read down the boxed letters to find another science word.

1. _____ [____] _____ _____ _____ _____ IST

2. _____ _____ _____ [____] OD

3. _____ _____ _____ [____] URE

4. EX_____ _____ [____] _____ _____

5. _____ [____|____] _____ _____ SCOPE

6. [____] _____ _____ _____ _____

7. _____ _____ [____] _____ ULE

8. _____ _____ [____] _____ _____ BE

SOLUTION: _____ _____ _____ _____ _____ _____ _____ _____ _____

Science Words

What a Comparison!
Write the list word that completes each analogy below.

1. *Telescope* is to *far* as _____ is to *near*.

2. *Studying* is to _____ as *painting* is to *artist*.

3. *Silly* is to _____ as *joy* is to *unhappiness*.

What Kind of Word?
Write the list word that matches each definition below. Then write *N* if the word is a noun or *A* if it is an adjective. The first one is done for you.

course of action _____**procedure**_____   **N**_____

1. important _____ _____

2. test, investigation _____ _____

3. a course of research _____ _____

4. magnifying instrument _____ _____

5. thin glass container _____ _____

6. orderly _____ _____

7. science expert _____ _____

8. technique _____ _____

9. particle _____ _____

10. having to do with molecules _____ _____

Write the list word that best completes each sentence.

1. Have you ever looked at mold under a _____?

2. The space shuttle astronauts conducted an _____ involving spiders.

3. My brother wants to be a _____ when he grows up.

4. We were eager to see if the _____ would work.

5. My mother is quite _____ about learning to fly.

Macmillan/McGraw-Hill

18

Level 11/Unit 6
Challenge Extension: Have students use the Challenge Words
to write a brief description of life on another planet.

133

Science Words

Proofreading Paragraph
For each pair of words in parentheses, underline the correctly spelled word.

Larger than Life

Like a (microscope, micrascope), a (magifying, magnifying) glass makes

objects appear larger than they actually are. Here is an (experiment,

experament) you can do in the kitchen. Line a clear drinking glass with plastic

wrap and (pour, pore) in two inches of water. Now, look down through the water

at a printed page. Compare the size of the print as viewed (thru, through) the

water with the size of print not covered by the glass. The print (shoud, should)

appear the same size. Next, being (careful, carefull) not to spill the water, raise

the level of the (plastic, plastick) wrap so that it is about an inch from the

(botom, bottom) of the glass. Now look down through the water and see what

the print looks like. The curved water (surfice, surface) created by the plastic

wrap acts as a magnifying lens, so the print should now appear larger.

Writing Activity
Write a paragraph about an experiment you enjoyed conducting or one you would like to
conduct. Use at least two list words.

_____

_____

_____

_____

_____

_____

_____

_____

_____

Science Words

In the list below, some of this week's spelling words are misspelled. If the word is correct, write *C* on the line. If the word is misspelled, write the correct spelling on the line.

1. scieintist _____

2. study _____

3. proceedure _____

4. expirament _____

5. test tube _____

6. microscoppe _____

7. invented _____

8. chemicle _____

9. serious _____

10. molacule _____

11. atem _____

12. biolagy _____

13. moleculer _____

14. methed _____

15. methodical _____

consentrated _____

gravity _____

microscoppic _____

reduced _____

rival _____

Word Scramble

Unscramble the list words below. Then read down the circled letters to find another list word.

1. YTSDU

2. HEMODT

3. REOPRECUD

4. YOIGLOB

5. MOAT

6. OCELLUME

7. PREMOOCICS

1.

2.

3.

4.

5.

6.

7.

____ ____ ____ ____ ____ ____ ____

Macmillan/McGraw-Hill

Outer-Space Words

Pretest Directions

Fold the paper in half. Use the blanks to write each word as it is said to you. When you finish the test, unfold the paper and correct any spelling mistakes. Practice those words for the Final Test.

1. _____	1. **extraterrestrial**
2. _____	2. **planet**
3. _____	3. **Martian**
4. _____	4. **rocket**
5. _____	5. **invading**
6. _____	6. **nonhuman**
7. _____	7. **laser**
8. _____	8. **magnetic**
9. _____	9. **flying saucer**
10. _____	10. **unidentified flying object**
11. _____	11. **comet**
12. _____	12. **galaxy**
13. _____	13. **earthling**
14. _____	14. **antennae**
15. _____	15. **marauder**

Challenge Words

Challenge Words	Challenge Words
_____	**cramped**
_____	**enchantment**
_____	**flailed**
_____	**universe**
_____	**alien**

To Parents,

Here are the results of your child's weekly spelling Pretest. You can help your child study for the Final Test by following these simple steps for each word on the word list:

1. Read the word to your child.
2. Have your child write the word, saying each letter as it is written.
3. Say each letter of the word as your child checks the spelling.
4. If a mistake has been made, have your child read each letter of the correctly spelled word aloud, and then repeat steps 1–3.

Children who read and write at home are usually good spellers. Encourage your child to write something every day.

Parent/Child Activity:

Help your child write a science fiction story using the outer-space words from the list. Make sure he or she revises and proofreads. Then have your child "publish" the story by sharing it with other family members or friends, either by letting them read it or by reading it aloud.

Outer-Space Words

The End
Write the list word or words that end with the letters given. Underline the letters in each word.

-er	*-ing*
1. _____	4. _____
2. _____	5. _____
3. _____	

In the Dictionary
Write the list word you would find between each pair of words in a dictionary. Then alphabetize the ten list words in the column on the right.

1. extract / extravagant _____   _____

2. plan / planetarium _____   _____

3. comedy / comfort _____   _____

4. eager / easily _____   _____

5. magic / magnify _____   _____

6. gadget / gallon _____   _____

7. intruder / involvement _____   _____

8. larva / laundry _____   _____

9. flutter / focus _____   _____

10. answer / antler _____   _____

What's That Sound?
Write the list word for each phonetic respelling.

1. /gal´ək sê/ _____   6. /rok´ it/ _____

2. /lā´ zər/ _____   7. /non hyü´ mən/ _____

3. /kom´ it/ _____   8. /an ten´ ē/ _____

4. /mag net´ ik/ _____   9. /mär´ shən/ _____

5. /urth´ ling/ _____   10. / plan´ it/ _____

Outer-Space Words

Write the spelling word that best fits each clue. Then enter the words in the puzzle and read down the circled letters to answer the riddle. Two words have been done for you here Add them in the puzzle.

having to do with magnets _____**magnetic**_____

creature from Mars _____**Martian**_____

1. intruding _____

2. kind of beam _____

3. billions of stars _____

4. missile _____

5. bandit, thief _____

6. feelers _____

7. creature from Earth _____

8. alien _____

9. airborne disk _____

10. looks like a star with a tail _____

11. ___ ___ [ ] ___ ___ ___ ___ ___ ___

12. ___ ___ ___ [ ] ___ ___ ___ ___

13. ___ ___ [ ] ___ ___ ___ ___ ___

14. ___ ___ [ ] ___ ___ ___ ___

15. ___ ___ ___ ___ [ ] ___ ___

16. ___ [ ] ___ ___ ___

17. ___ ___ ___ [ ] ___ ___ ___

18. [ ] ___ ___ ___ ___ ___ ___

19. ___ ___ ___ ___ [ ] ___ ___ ___

20. ___ ___ ___ ___ ___ ___ ___ [ ] ___

21. [ ] ___ ___ ___ ___ ___ ___ ___

22. ___ ___ ___ ___ [ ] ___ ___

WHAT DID THE BOOSTER ROCKET SAY TO THE SPACE SHUTTLE?

CAN I ___ ___ ___ ___ ___ ___ ___ ___ ___ ___ ___

___ ___ ___ ___ ___ ?

Challenge Extension: Have students use the Challenge Words to
write a review of a favorite science-fiction movie or TV show.

Level 11/Unit 6

22

Macmillan/McGraw-Hill

Outer-Space Words

Proofreading Paragraph
For each pair of words in parentheses, underline the correctly spelled word.

Recycled Rockets

The space shuttle is (made, maid) up of three main parts. The part we are

most (familure, familiar) with is the orbiter, which looks almost like a (plain,

plane). After each mission, the orbiter lands on an airstrip and is (prepaired,

prepared) for another mission. Each orbiter is expected to be used a (hundred,

hundrid) times. The other main parts of the shuttle system are the solid (rockett,

rocket) boosters and a large (fuel, fule) tank. The tank, which is released just

before the shuttle goes into orbit, is the only (mane, main) part of the shuttle

system that is never reused. Before the first space shuttle was (bilt, built), no

part of any rocket was used for more than one mission. Now expensive (pieces,

peaces) of equipment can be used many times.

Writing Activity
Would you like to travel in space? Write a paragraph that begins "I would (or would not) like to travel in space because . . ."

_____

_____

_____

_____

_____

_____

_____

_____

_____

Macmillan/McGraw-Hill

Outer-Space Words

One word in each set is spelled correctly. Circle the correctly spelled word and write it on the line.

1. extraterrestrial
extraterestrial
extraterrestriel
extraterrestriall

_____

2. planat
planet
plannet
planit

_____

3. Martion
martian
Martain
Martian

_____

4. rocket
rockit
rockett
rockket

_____

5. envading
invaiding
invading
invating

_____

6. nonhuman
non-human
nonhueman
nonhumen

_____

7. lazer
lasser
laser
lasur

_____

8. magnettic
magnetic
magnetec
magnetick

_____

9. flying sauser
fliing saucer
flying saucer
flyying saucer

_____

10. unidentified-flying-object
unidentified flying object
unidintified flying object
unidentified flying objeckt

_____

11. commet
comit
comet
camet

_____

12. gallaxy
galaxie
galixy
galaxy

_____

13. earthling
eartheling
erthling
earthlling

_____

14. antenny
antennaie
antennae
anttennae

_____

15. marodder
marauder
marrauder
maraudder

_____

crampt
crammped
kramped
cramped

_____

enchantment
enchantmint
enchantmant
inchantment

_____

flailled
flayled
flailed
flaled

_____

alian
alien
allien
alein

_____

univerce
unniverse
universe
unaverse

_____

Macmillan/McGraw-Hill

Content Words: Space Words

Pretest

1. _____ 4. _____ 7. _____ 9. _____

2. _____ 5. _____ 8. _____ 10. _____

3. _____ 6. _____

Parts of Speech

Organize the list words according to parts of speech. You will notice that some of the words may appear in more than one category.

NOUNS		VERBS
_____	_____	_____
_____	_____	_____
_____	_____	**ADJECTIVES**
_____		_____
_____		_____

Space Scramble

Unscramble these letters to form list words.

fapscartec _____

tansryomo _____

lasteleit _____

Word Journal

Imagine that you are an astronaut taking a trip into the unknown. Write down the one object in space you would like to explore. Then make a list below of words that describe what you see on your journey.

_____

_____

_____

_____

_____

_____

Macmillan/McGraw-Hill

Content Words: Space Words

Word List

1. solar
2. constellation
3. lunar
4. satellite
5. aircraft
6. orbit
7. shuttle
8. spacecraft
9. comet
10. astronomy

It's All About Space

You can be an expert in astronomy by filling in the blanks! You may want to refer to your dictionary, almanac, or other reference sources for help. Some words may be in the plural form or used twice.

The _____ system consists of nine planets and their moons, the asteroids and

_____, all of which _____ the sun. Astronomers send up _____

and travel in _____ to study our _____ system.

Lost in Space

Eight words from the word list are hidden in this puzzle. Circle the words as you find them.

```
A  E  S  O  C  C  O  M  E  T  L  Y  O
S  H  U  T  T  L  E  S  L  U  N  A  R
O  R  L  B  S  D  B  P  Y  N  S  Q  B
L  T  A  I  R  C  R  A  F  T  N  H  I
A  I  R  S  P  A  C  E  C  R  A  F  T
R  P  D  E  S  A  T  E  L  L  I  T  E
```

Proofer in Action!

The four spelling mistakes in these space facts are out of this world! Circle each one, and write it correctly on the line that follows.

There are 88 different groups of constallations.

Before sattelites carried telescopes into space to help astronomers learn about

the universe, aercraft, balloons, and rockets were used.

Comits are balls of icy particles and dust that travel around the sun.

_____

Review Words

Pretest

1. _____ 6. _____ 11. _____

2. _____ 7. _____ 12. _____

3. _____ 8. _____ 13. _____

4. _____ 9. _____ 14. _____

5. _____ 10. _____ 15. _____

Pattern Power!

Write the list words containing these double letters.

_____ **ee** _____

_____ **tt** _____

_____ **rr** _____

_____ **nn** _____

What Fits?

Can you figure out which list word goes in each blank? Read the sentences aloud. Think about the clues that tell you what kind of word you are looking for.

You thought Ms. Cryer was joking, but she was _____.

The thief was _____ at the end of the mystery story.

Jon _____ Larry for the present.

The answers on this test are either true or _____.

Since it comes from the sun, can _____ power work at night?

One small _____ can lead to huge problems.

Her _____ of solving math problems usually worked.

Word Journal

Write the words from **Pattern Power!** below. Look at the letters that are doubled. Can every letter in the alphabet be doubled in some word? Try to write down as many examples as you can. Are there any letters that are never doubled?

_____

Review Words

Word List

1. method	**5.** planet	**9.** reliable	**13.** revealed
2. serious	**6.** laser	**10.** false	**14.** satellite
3. thanked	**7.** solar	**11.** atom	**15.** shuttle
4. antennae	**8.** peeked	**12.** error	

Speak Out!

Write the list words that match each pronunciation. Remember to say the words out loud when spelling them, too!

/lā´ zər/ _____   /ri lī´ə bəl/ _____

/at´əm/ _____   /sat´ə līt/ _____

Build-a-Word

Can you use these letter pairs to create four list words?

od	nn	un	an	ed
iv	pe	me	ae	er
th	te	se	ek	

_____   _____   _____   _____

Proofer in Action!

This essay is almost complete. It just needs to be proofread. How many spelling mistakes are there? Circle them all.

With sattelights many mysteries of the univirse are being reveeled. Experiments

with lazers are giving relyable information about the make-up of our sollar

system. Other satellites have seen the surface of other planets. The photos they

took were transmitted to antenae here on Earth.

Macmillan/McGraw-Hill